BUT THEN SOMETHING HAPPENED

A Story of Everyday Dementia

CHRIS CARLING

G⦿LDEN
BOOKS

First published in Great Britain in 2012 by
GOLDEN BOOKS
www.goldenbooks.co.uk

Golden Books
47 Searle Street
Cambridge CB4 3DB

A CIP Catalogue of this book is available
from the British Library

ISBN 978-0-9573079-0-2

Cover image: ©istockphoto.com/ Iain Sarjeant/ Jkitan

Design & Typesetting in Fairfield 11½pt by
www.chandlerbookdesign.co.uk

Printed by
Lightning Source

For Fred and Mary

CONTENTS

Part 1
Fred, Mary and Me

Part 2
Standing Back

NOTE: Some names of hospital and care home residents
have been changed to protect privacy.

BUT THEN SOMETHING HAPPENED

A Story of Everyday Dementia

Part 1

Fred, Mary and Me

Chapter One
Crisis Weekend

An everyday story

Fred and Mary are my parents and this is our story, an everyday story of dementia in the family, how dementia changes everything in ordinary and extraordinary ways. Our story is both commonplace – old people with minds befuddled by dementia are everywhere once you start looking – and unique. Every family affected by Alzheimer's or other types of dementia plays out a different drama and has a different story to tell.

Ours has had a particular poignancy because my Mum, Mary, and my Dad, Fred, were both affected in different ways with different types of dementia at the same time. For me, their daughter, living nearby, as the drama of their joint dementia played out, they gradually shifted from parents into people, individuals who'd each had hopes and dreams which were finally coming to an end.

When I started writing this memoir I believed Fred and Mary were the central characters with me, their amateur carer, as a mere supporting artist. Only belatedly did I see that this is very much my story, that I was – am – very much a participant, that the role of witness, propper-up, the one who keeps their mind as others lose theirs, has its own special kind of suffering. For a long time I didn't want to acknowledge this; for a long time my image of myself was as 'OK, fine, I can handle it'.

This may have been because I never consciously chose the role of carer. Rather I fell into it, almost by accident, starting by helping out as my parents got older, the way in families you do, and then helping some more, and more as their minds became muddled. And suddenly, or so it seemed, I was the 'responsible adult' in the family.

Even this I only fully realised with hindsight. I was so busy coping, keeping a cool, confident, swan-like exterior, that I failed to notice the furious paddling beneath the water line. There was another factor too. To me carers were selfless people who devoted their entire lives, twenty four hours a day to caring for their loved ones. And that wasn't me. I was not selfless, and I had my own life, my own home to maintain. And therefore I underplayed my role, saw myself as just helping out. And where's the stress in that, compared to what 'real' carers go through? Except that I didn't always know what to do. Like thousands of other amateur, part-time yet crucial carers, I felt responsible for my charges yet lacked the experience to know what is best for a couple who are both in different ways losing their minds. This is therefore the story not just of my parents' progressive joint dementia, but of my trial and error efforts to carry them until their accumulated weight grew too heavy. That part of the story is dedicated to 'amateur carers' everywhere.

At the same time, like all good stories, Fred and Mary's is also a love story, though I didn't appreciate at first the strength of their love. For children, even extremely grown up children like myself, Mums and Dads are parents first, lovers only a distant second. What I did know was that Fred had always been a bit of a romantic: the kind of man who'd slip a small volume of poetry into his pocket as he prepared to go out on flying missions as a young RAF Navigator in World War II. I knew too that he'd loved Mary since the moment he set eyes on her, in a fairground, in 1934 when he was just seventeen. And here they both were, more than seventy years later facing mental meltdown: was their fairy tale about to reach a brutal end?

An inconspicuous start

Our everyday story of dementia in the family starts in the telling with a sudden drama yet the foundations were being quietly laid years before. Dementia, particularly Alzheimer's, is insidious, creeping up slowly, wrapping its tendrils round you, gently at first then squeezing harder. The saga of my parents' joint dementia, therefore, has no definitive starting point. Or none that any of us were aware of at the time.

What is clear is that by 2005 we – Mum, Dad and me – were definitely beginning to struggle as Dad's spirits sank lower and his GP prescribed increasing doses of anti-depressants. At this stage depression was the diagnosis not dementia. In early 2006, worn out by trying to keep their household going as well as my own, I'd requested a Social Services visit to see if I could get them some help. Though the social worker declined to recommend a 'care plan' she noted Dad's depression and referred him to our local Older People's Mental Health Team. The Community Psychiatric Nurse appointed to assess his mental state felt that what looked like depression didn't quite fit the pattern and might be something more. To check her suspicions she referred him to a specialist in old age psychiatry. In the summer of 2006, just before his 89th birthday, Dr Dening visited him at home and diagnosed, not Alzheimer's but a vascular dementia, possibly caused by mini-strokes that had gone unnoticed.

At the same time though largely unremarked, Mary was developing the symptoms of either Alzheimer's disease or a similar form of dementia. Like two out of three dementia sufferers, she has never been formally diagnosed. The closest she came to a diagnosis was that day Dr Dening visited Fred and informally observed from her speech and behaviour that she was 'probably in the early stages of Alzheimer's'. She was not his patient, however, so no action followed.

Muddling along

During this earlier phase Mary and Fred were still living in their own home, muddling along with a couple of hours a week outside help fixed eventually, not through Social Services but from an excellent local charity called Crossroads, backed up by me. It came as a shock as I began to see, only dimly at first, that both their minds were failing in different ways. Though their welfare had been weighing on my mind and sitting on my shoulders for a good couple of years I hadn't known what was wrong. This was several years before dementia hit the headlines and became the talking point it is today.

In my amateur carer role I'd been visiting more and more, and worrying when I wasn't, steering the family ship on an increasingly shaky course. But Mum didn't really seem to notice the propping up, believing, I now realise due to her dementia, that she and Dad were coping independently, complaining that Dad wasn't doing the vacuuming often enough. Having no experience of dementia I didn't recognise the signs.

After Dad's vascular dementia had been diagnosed that day he became the focus of my attention while Mum's odd behaviour tucked itself away at the back of my mind. At that stage Dad's dementia did not result in major confusion – instead the effects were more specific, attacking those parts of his brain responsible for higher functions such as word finding, planning and motivation. He was aware he and Mum weren't coping very well but his impaired ability to plan and make decisions meant he no longer had the capacity to do much about it. Not that he ever mentioned his vascular dementia, and taking my lead from him I didn't mention it either. His response to what must have felt like a hopeless situation was to escape from it all by spending much of his life asleep.

Though Dad's vascular dementia and Mum's 'early stages of Alzheimer's' were not discussed, their effects were definitely showing – a household of two people with different kinds of dementia does not run smoothly. When they gave up on their weekly shopping trips to Tesco, I ordered their food and groceries from Tesco Online; when they could no longer organise eating, I ordered their mid-day meals from Wiltshire Farm Foods. These were delivered fortnightly and stored in their freezer. Dad learnt how to 'cook' them in the microwave (vascular dementia leaves more faculties intact than Alzheimer's, in the early stages at least) while Mum continued to believe that she prepared their lunch. When they stopped going out – Mum because she came to believe she would topple over backwards if she went out, in staying indoors she believed, falsely, that she was acting on her doctor's orders – I collected their prescriptions and loaded 'dosset boxes' for Dad to take his pills (many) and to give Mum hers (only thyroid); if light bulbs failed or appliances faltered, I went round there to fix things. When Dad had physical health problems I accompanied him on numerous hospital visits (emergency admission for anaemia, endoscopy, macular degeneration) as well as hearing aid and eye tests and GP visits. With difficulty, I washed their hair; with little skill I acted as their hair stylist…

If anyone had asked me why I was doing all this, I wouldn't have known the answer because I hadn't asked myself the question. They were my parents. They needed help. Who else was going to do it? What would other 'amateur carers' say?

But then something happened

During this build up period – which only became a build up with hindsight – the important thing for me was that we were getting by, or so I chose to believe. Doctors, social workers, psychiatric nurses, none of them seemed to be taking our family's double dementia particularly seriously. So why should we?

But then something happened.

Or rather a series of things happened, starting one summer weekend, that brought the fragile edifice we'd constructed tumbling down. I shouldn't have been surprised to see our house of cards collapse, but I was. Had I been in denial? Some might say so but actually it's more complex than that. Though I was aware that dementia was attacking the brains of both parents at different rates and in different ways, they seemed nevertheless able to function, after a fashion. What I failed to factor in was that they were functioning because I was propping them up. And also because they were two: two even with damaged minds could still support each other. Up to a point.

And so unconsciously I gave them the benefit of the doubt. Took them at face value. Maybe they weren't too bad after all. Until it was obvious they were worse than I thought. Or Mum at least, her Alzheimer's-type dementia more advanced than we'd realised.

By the time their dementia story stopped rumbling quietly along and erupted into a full scale crisis it was mid-2007, the year both Mum and Dad celebrated their 90th birthdays, Mum on 2nd February, Dad on 23rd August. Their love story was well advanced by then – they'd been married for 68 years.

But between those two birthday celebrations, one July weekend, life as they, and I, had known it finally came to an end.

Crisis Weekend

The Weekend that changed everything began on Friday 13th, an inauspicious date on which Mum, Dad and I shifted from 'muddling along' to the next stage of 'something needs to be done'. We were typical, it turns out, in that people with dementia can often muddle along for years until... Until what? Until something happens, a fall, an accident, a flood in the kitchen, the gas left on, a small or not so small drama that moves the action inexorably forward. Like a play or film, there's a crisis, an 'inciting incident' that triggers the action that follows.

Not that I saw this at the time. You don't when you're one of the players. That Weekend my mother was the central character with my Dad and I as supporting leads. The day before, Mum had been still reasonably active around the house, today she suddenly declares she can't walk: her knee is swollen and painful, as I can see when I pop in to check they are OK.

Dad hovers on the sidelines, depressed and withdrawn, worried how they are going to manage. Mum's thyroid pills are still in the 'dosset box'. 'Have you not been giving them to her, Dad?' I ask as though somehow it's his fault. Still focused on somehow getting by, fitting in Mum and Dad's care with my own life, I desperately want everything to be OK but it so clearly isn't. 'She's up half the night', he says. 'I don't know where she sleeps'.

Time, I think – naively as it turns out – to call in the Professionals. I'll get the doctor out to see Mum. It's not as though she's been a massive drain on the NHS – she hadn't seen her GP for about four years. I'd been to the surgery in her place to report her increasing confusion but no GP had actually seen the degree of her mental breakdown. The doctor can look at her knee and sort out her mobility, I reason, and at the same time actually observe her dementia and finally make some professional assessment of her mental confusion. I ring the surgery mentioning these two problems, the knee and an opportunity for the doctor to observe her mental state: they promise a home visit any time after 12.30 pm.

Scene 1: Friday 13th July 2007:
The doctor cometh

12.30, a ring on the bell: the doctor, youngish, slim, dark haired, brisk. Mum and Dad have daytime TV on, as lots of housebound people do. Doctor demands it be switched off. Tone bossy and peremptory. None of the kindness and compassion we crave. On this inauspicious day, this visit is getting off to an inauspicious start.

Mum is sitting in a low chair. Ignoring Dad and me, doctor crouches down beside her, addressing all her remarks to 'the patient', which would have been admirable had the patient been in possession of all her faculties. She talks at top speed, too fast even for me. I already have bad feelings about this visit. Hasn't she read Mum's notes? Didn't my message about Mum's dementia get through?

Doctor rattles on about 'arthritis' and 'compression stockings' she apparently thinks Mum should be wearing. Mum, for her part, looks very plausible, as though she's understanding – people with dementia, I've discovered, seem to retain an uncanny ability to put on a good show for strangers. 'Your pain in the knee is caused by arthritis', doctor slows down and speaks louder. Perhaps she thinks Mum is deaf. 'Arthritis', Mum repeats slowly, looking up at me for enlightenment.

'Can you bend your knee for me', doctor asks. Mum smiles vacantly. Doctor asks again. And again. Has she never come across dementia before, the way it makes you forget the meanings of simple instructions? When Mum does not obey does it not occur to her to wonder why? Apparently not. I'm reluctant to spell out the problem but she leaves me no choice: 'She doesn't understand you. She doesn't understand what you've been talking about. She's got dementia'. I speak quietly, trying to be discreet as we still haven't talked about her dementia directly to Mum. The closest we've come is to laugh with her about problems with her memory.

Doctor stands up, abandoning her 'concerned crouching' position: patients with dementia can apparently be talked about in their presence as if they weren't there. Instinctively I step forward, putting myself protectively between this doctor and my Mum, trying to minimise the damage. Mum has always been super-sensitive, easily upset by unthinking remarks. Dementia hasn't changed that. And she is certainly not completely gaga.

Doctor snaps into 'social care' mode seeming affronted now that her time should be wasted on a condition that's surely the domain of social workers. 'What are you worried about?' she demands. 'Do you want her to go into a home?' At this point Mum going into a home hasn't crossed my mind. We've been muddling along, haven't we? 'Do you like living here?' she asks Mum. 'Yes', says Mum. 'Or do you want to go somewhere where they could look after you better?' Mum looks puzzled.

'All you'll get is a diagnosis'

Doctor plunges into the realms of Social Services and care assessments. Hang on, I'm thinking, isn't dementia a medical condition, a malfunction of the brain? 'Can she have a mental health assessment?' I ask. Doctor is doubtful: 'All you'll get is a diagnosis', she says.

All we'll get is a diagnosis. All. All. Isn't that what we want: to understand better what's wrong with Mum? Isn't it important to know? Apparently not: it's only later I learn the statistic that two out of three dementia sufferers in the UK are never properly diagnosed. Though with recent government initiatives this statistic may have changed, Mum to this day remains one of the many dementia sufferers without a formal diagnosis.

As a gesture towards assessing Mum's mental health doctor quickly goes through what I've come to call to myself the 'Alzheimer's questions' that are supposed to show how near or far removed a patient is from reality. The official name for this test I discover many months later is the 'mini mental state examination' or MMSE. Essentially the MMSE is a series of questions about simple facts such as time and place and who people are that any 'normal' citizen should know. Doctor asks Mum her address. No response. Mum smiles her way through this and the rest of the interrogation. Your date of birth. Mum smiles. Your age? I'll whisper it, she says, but doesn't. What year is it? Don't know. Mum fails the entire test till the last item: 'Can you count backwards from 20 for me'. That Mum can do: she worked as a comptometer operator in the days before calculators and computers and she's very handy with numbers. Though that skill hasn't left her, however, it's not enough to save her from doctor's judgement of definitely demented.

But dementia, probably of the Alzheimer's type if we are to believe Dr Dening's observations are correct, is not, apparently, a medical diagnosis. Doctor does not seem too concerned about how Mum — and the rest of us — will cope with her seriously malfunctioning brain. At one point she looks over to my 90 year old Dad, his diagnosis a year ago of vascular dementia presumably in his notes, and says: 'You're alright, aren't you?' I hear her words as completely uncaring as though she is saying: 'Surely you, old man with vascular dementia, are alright to look after your severely demented wife'. I guess this was the price Dad paid for looking both years younger than his age and much fitter than he actually felt.

Doctor says she'll make a referral to Social Services and invites me to make one too. Or to follow up hers. She's back to her mile-a-minute mode of talking. I'm not really very clear what she's saying — something about referrals getting through quicker if they come from a doctor. We come full circle, back to Mum's knee (those compression stockings again — she gives me a prescription for stockings) and — oh yes, better check Mum doesn't have a urine infection (urinary tract infections (UTIs) are known to be common in old folks and liable to result in mental confusion). Can Mum provide a urine sample? Doctor proffers a container for the sample but doesn't offer any clues as to how to get the required sample out of an old lady with a hole in her brain where the idea of urine sampling used to be.

Marks out of ten?

And she is gone. I wonder how many marks out of ten she'd give herself for this consultation. Upset and angry at her brisk treatment of my vulnerable parents, I go off to Boots for compression stockings. I scarcely notice my route as I go over and over in my mind the sheer awfulness of this doctor's performance. I was the one who called her out too. Guilt at exposing them colours my anger as mentally I compose an official complaint.

There is something else too. By her obtuseness this doctor has forced Mum's dementia much further out into the open than I've allowed so far. Up till now I'd kept it closed up in a corner of my mind – I both knew about it, and yet acted much of the time as though it wasn't so. Part Two (in the chapter 'Why didn't we see it coming?') explores this self-protective ability many of us have both to know painful things yet at the same time act as if they are not true.

My mood is not improved when Boots prescription counter rejects the prescription for stockings. Apparently the doctor should have referred Mum to the District Nurses who are then supposed to come and measure. My already lengthy 'official complaint' expands to include failure to be up-to-date with stocking supply procedures.

This was the first, but sadly will not be the last, time I come up against the apparent indifference of the medical profession to mental confusion. For them dementia seems to equal social care. Carers coming in. People to do the personal things patients with failing minds can no longer do for themselves. But what about 'mental care'? What about advice for living with dementia? Advice for those living with dementia sufferers?

Even the word 'demented' is an unfortunate one, suggesting, as it does, madness. People with dementia are not mad. They have frail and failing minds in the way that others have frail and failing bodies. And yet…Failing minds do raise questions of identity that failing bodies don't. If Mum tells a nurse, as she did later while in hospital, that she and my Dad don't have any children yet, where does that leave me? When she whispers to me, looking over at Dad, 'Are you married to him?' what does that say about their nearly 70 years of marriage?

It's questions like these that make dementia both frightening and fascinating. Frightening because of the apparent ease with which whole swathes of our past can be wiped out, yet fascinating, the way an individual can live in different time zones at the same time (Mum could tell the nurse they have no children yet accept the nurse telling her in the next breath: 'I was talking to your daughter on the phone…'). Fascinating too in the way a new person can emerge, recognisable yet unmistakeably different.

Scene 1A: Later that day: The urine sample

Whatever we think of them, doctors do have a certain authority. If doctor wants a urine sample from Mum, even if I think it's pointless, then I feel some obligation to provide one. But how? This is my mother: proud, private and puzzled by the world. She's a native English speaker no longer able to understand the simple English sentence: 'The doctor wants a urine sample'. I can't just give her the container, send her to the bathroom and expect her to produce some pee. And anyway, it's a messy business at the best of times, getting a sample of urine into one of those specimen bottles.

Dad is still closely enough in touch with the world to understand what's needed. Saying 'urine sample' clearly isn't going to get us very far, so we try varying the terminology. Doctor wants some of your wee-wee…your pee…your pittle. 'Pittle' hits the spot. Doctor wants some of your pittle. 'Can you do a pittle, Mum?'

'I've just been', she says. Curses. We all start laughing. 'Can you do a bit more? Into this' – the specimen bottle looks ridiculously small. More laughter. 'Do it in a cup', Dad says. A burst of laughter from me, but actually it's not a bad idea. If she could wee into a bigger container I could then transfer some into the bottle. 'Better make sure we wash it up before we make a cup of tea!' It's becoming a big joke.

Cup in hand I help Mum upstairs, persuading her back into walking mode though her knee is clearly painful. She manages to get up to the bathroom. We pull down her pants and I try to encourage her to hold the cup between her legs – I've no idea if she understands what we are trying to achieve. She can't grasp she needs to hold it so I try to keep it in position and we start giggling. 'Can you do a bit, Mum. Doesn't have to be much. Just a drop'. But nothing comes. Not a single splatter. The cup is completely dry and we're practically in hysterics.

Never mind, I say. We'll try again later. Sorry, doctor. I did my best.

Back to front burner

At this stage in the drama, in my mind I've dismissed 'the Professionals' as useless. On reflection well after the event, I wonder if I still saw myself as able to rescue the situation, assuming as I had so far that we could cope largely on our own, the perceived inadequacy of the Professionals serving to reinforce my natural bent? As a family we'd always been independently-minded, not easily putting ourselves in other people's hands. I guess I wanted things 'back to normal' however haywire normal was becoming. Mmm. You can learn a lot about yourself once you stand back and take a dispassionate look at the way you care for those you love.

Staying in 'rescuer' mode that Friday 13th, I go home and think about how to maintain Mum's mobility now she's got such a painful leg. Should I be getting hold of a wheelchair? Maybe then I could take her out. I imagine walks along the river, Mum enjoying the fresh air, commenting on the boats…she hasn't been out of the house for a year, she who had so loved to go on little outings to 'look round the shops.' She hadn't been persuadable to go out, due to that belief she'd adopted that she'd overbalance and topple over backwards. But if she had a wheelchair. Why hadn't I thought of this before? I consult the internet and phone the Red Cross and various other wheelchair-providing organisations.

A shadow, however, falls across these idyllic river walk fantasies: I need to grapple with another, less agreeable, more urgent problem. Earlier in the day, on top of everything else, I'd noticed Mum's skirt was wet at the back, and so, reluctantly, I bring forward from the back burner, where it had simmered very gently for some time in response to finding dirty pants hidden in odd corners, to the front burner, the fact that Mum is becoming incontinent. At least some of the time.

Scene 2: Saturday 14th July 2007: Incontinence Saturday

For the first time that Saturday morning, I think about incontinence, not in a general way but very specifically as it relates to Mum. What it means. What to do. What shall I do? This drama is becoming a crisis. I phone a friend.

Briskly she initiates me into the world of incontinence pads, those bought from Boots, according to her, being superior to those provided free by the District Nurses. Not that so far we have consulted any District Nurses.

Reluctantly abandoning my usual leisurely Saturday morning Guardian read, I go upstairs to my office to consult my other friend, the internet, to find – I should have guessed – that there is a whole world of incontinence products out there, pads and disposable pants of all shapes, sizes and absorbencies. They'd been there all the time, of course, but I'd had no reason to see them.

A barely formed thought floats through my mind: 'Mum may have to go into a home sooner than we think'. I note it in the diary, the 'Dementia Diary', I'd started to keep so I'd recall the events of this time. It was that awful doctor who planted the first seed. And here it was starting to sprout. Mum or Dad going into a home had not even been on our radar till she mentioned it. And even now it was just a small grey cloud.

From my internet wanderings I also print out an article written by a woman caring for her husband who has Alzheimer's. 'Pooh is not toxic waste', it was called, setting me pondering about what we call what comes out of us and, in the normal course of events, goes down the toilet: this woman chose 'pooh'. Not that Mum is 'doubly incontinent' – nice euphemism – but maybe one day she will be. I'm certainly starting to realise that this is a 'big crisis', a real recognition that she is not functioning on a very basic level. Dealing with bodily waste: you can't get much more basic than that.

But I can cope, can't I? Of course. And so it is that on one of the busiest Saturdays of the year, Cambridge heaving with tourists in cheerful gaggles, my partner, Terry, and I are in Boots hunting down incontinence pads. Bemused by the choice, I select a packet from the 'medium' range, which seems a safe bet. And we buy a new packet of pants for Mum from M&S.

Later I go round to Mum and Dad's and try to explain to Mum that she needs to start wearing a pad. I demonstrate by putting a pad into one of the new pairs of pants – I've got a larger size to accommodate a pad. I manage to get the pants plus pad on her – which is not hard as she isn't wearing any pants. One of the things I learnt early is that people with dementia can forget to put on articles of clothing, or put on several of the same thing.

I do all this in a matter-of-fact way, as though it is the most natural thing in the world. Mum doesn't question, doesn't resist, doesn't protest. We are suddenly in a different world together, a world in which I'm helping her pull up her pants as she once helped me pull up mine. Though my mind might be lagging behind, my actions show that I do recognise the extent of Mum's mental damage.

I put pads into two more of the new pairs and leave them for her to change into when necessary. What could I have been thinking? Did I really believe she was understanding me and would dutifully put on these fresh pads? Much more likely, I was still in the grip of wishful thinking, desperately wanting things to be OK, clinging on to my own life, terrified of being submerged by my parents' needs. Or rather what I saw as their needs: though I'd brought incontinence to the front burner, peeing in your pants may have been way down their list of concerns.

Mum wanted to lie down after these exertions. Maybe she thought it was bedtime rather than afternoon. Dementia sufferers can get very confused about the time of day. I went up to her later and saw she was lying with her head hard up against the headboard. She looked uncomfortable and I helped her put her head properly on the pillow. I think she had forgotten how to move down the bed. I was learning that dementia can affect you in very basic ways. Simple movements that were automatic suddenly no longer are. People can eventually forget how to eat and drink. I didn't want to think about that stage.

Scene 3: Sunday 15th July 2007: Lunch on the floor

So far on that Crisis Weekend, I'd been going back and forth to my parents' house, dealing with doctors and incontinence and Mum's painful knee, while at the same time clinging limpet-like to my own life, to my yoga and other pleasurable routines, to my whole identity as an independent person. I was still just an amateur carer after all. Wasn't I? Just helping Mum and Dad out.

Well, no, actually, at this point I was their lynch pin – I just didn't want to recognise it for fear of becoming a 'real' carer.

As the 'responsible adult' of the family I was catching a glimpse of what it might be like to slip unwarily into a 'proper' caring role. Unwarily because being self-employed with a portfolio career as a consultant/coach/occasional mediator I had plenty of flexibility to organise my work as I chose and to take time off to deal with doctors and hair washing and rush round in emergencies. Already I was taking more and more time off.

So far I had viewed this flexibility as a positive. I could be there for my parents, popping round, sorting out problems. But I was becoming increasingly terrified of being swallowed up by the task of caring for them. Not because they demanded it: they never actually demanded anything. But because I had taken it on and now it was taking over: their predicament was becoming part of me. Any time I had a conversation with a friend or colleague I hadn't seen for a while, I'd immediately start talking about them. Mum and Dad were constantly on my mind. I was carrying them on my shoulders. And it was scary. I was the one keeping them afloat, but in spite of all my efforts, I was failing – we were all beginning to sink.

Have you told Chris?

The Sunday morning of that Weekend, I went to yoga, as usual. A great class. I walked into town with my friend, Carole, as usual, and, as so often, we talked about my Mum. Terry and I met up in the Caffe Nero, as usual, and we talked about his poems and life in general. One of my most pleasurable routines. Slowly I began to slip out of my role as amateur caring daughter and relax into me as me.

Back home I was reading the Sunday papers and thinking about making our lunch. It was 1.30 pm and I was hungry having not eaten all day. And then the phone rang. It was my brother, Alan, a couple of years younger than me and living about 50 miles away in Stamford. He'd just called my parents to say he and his wife, Sue, would be visiting them later that afternoon. Dad had told him that Mum was sitting on the floor and he couldn't lift her up. 'Have you told Chris?' 'No', Dad says. Instead he's served her lunch on the floor – and her breakfast before that, it transpires. He said he'd found her 'in the morning'.

This was Dad's vascular dementia kicking in, I realised later: he genuinely can't plan or make decisions. If something happens, he doesn't know what to do. We shouldn't therefore have been surprised he hadn't tried to get help, but we were. He could seem so normal we didn't realise for some time the full extent of his brain's deterioration.

I drive straight round – luckily it's only a five minute drive – and find her propped up, her back against the sofa seat, remarkably perky considering she's been sitting there for hours. I have the feeling the situation doesn't seem that odd to either of them. 'She's all wet', Dad says. So much for my illusion that she'd put on the pants I'd carefully furnished with pads.

Using my pelvic floor muscles to protect my back and the upper body strength I've developed through years of yoga, I manage to lift her up on to the couch. She's very heavy, like a dead weight. And her leg is still horribly painful. She also smells. I'm going to have to wash her and change her clothes.

To a 'real' carer, washing your Mum after she's peed herself may seem commonplace. To an amateur carer like me it's a first. She's in pain, back to saying she can't walk, so we can't get upstairs to the bathroom. Yet she needs to be washed and her clothes changed. I know my parents don't have a washing up bowl, but they do have a plastic bucket.

I run some warm water into the bucket, get hold of a flannel, soap, some clean clothes, including one of the pairs of pants lined with a pad, take Mum's blouse off and do a rather cursory underarm wash. I don't change her bra. At this stage my attention is more directed towards her bottom half, which meant I didn't notice the angry red rash in the deep fold under one of her breasts that showed up later: a fungal infection that was the source of an odd smell I'd been noticing but couldn't place. But that was then, and this was now. I dried her top half and threaded her arms through a clean blouse.

Now it was time for the bottom half. I decide for modesty's sake to get Dad out of the way, though I guess in nearly 70 years of marriage there's not much of each other they haven't seen. It must have been my own possible embarrassment I was guarding against. It's a struggle to get her skirt off; I get her to stand up and hold on to me so I can remove her pants, then from a rather awkward angle, wash then dry her bottom and legs, talking all the while in that cheerful, encouraging way that seems to come naturally to carers but may be highly irritating to those they care for: 'We'll just pull these up now' … 'There you go' … 'How's that?' … 'Well done'… 'All finished'.

Washing ordeal over, clean and dry, I get her into a chair. She's insisting she can't walk, and I'm panicking inside as to how we are going to manage if she can't get to bed, can't get to the bathroom. Something else is weighing on me too: I'm planning to be away next week for a couple of days on a retreat that I feel a profound need for – it's my way of trying to look after myself to give me the strength to better look after Mum and Dad. How on earth are they going to manage?

Yesterday Mum said she couldn't walk, yet she did walk upstairs, working out as she did so how to distribute the weight so her leg didn't hurt so much. Clearly some of her mental faculties were still working. I persuade her to try this again to give her some confidence back. We go upstairs together – she makes it but I'm fearful she could fall if she tried it alone. Things really are falling apart. I wonder if I can organise a commode and some nursing care for her for the few days I'm away.

Scene 3A: Later that afternoon: 'I thought I was dying'

I'm starving by now, so I get her settled, reassure Dad that Alan will be here soon, and go back home for some lunch. Not long after Alan rings to say they arrived to find Mum on the floor again. She's fallen, apparently, on her way to answer the door. 'I thought I was dying', she tells me when I get there. 'As white as a sheet'.

Alan wants to call out the out-of-hours Duty Doctor. I'm unconvinced given what happened when I called the GP on Friday, but Alan works in Social Services and has more faith in 'the system' than I do. Two falls in one day, he says – we need to find out why. You ring them then, I say. And he does. Though I've done most of the caring for Mum and Dad, there have been crucial points at which he's insisted on bringing in 'the Professionals', where I would have struggled on for longer, trying to cope. This was one of those pivotal points.

We waited over two hours for the Duty Doctor's visit but when he finally came it was a lovely young Irishman who took Mum seriously. I regret that I didn't take in his name when he introduced himself as I'd like to put him forward for sainthood – his competent compassion was so much what we needed after the awfulness of Friday's doctorial experience.

He gently examined her, diagnosed a fever indicating an infection somewhere, said she needed to be admitted to hospital for a few days for the experts to find out what was causing the infection. They'd get her back into shape, he assured us. When he said 'hospital' I was taken aback. For me 'going into hospital' was about being really ill. Surely she wasn't that bad. Even in the midst of crisis I was trying not to make a drama out of it. As the doctor did the necessary paperwork it started to feel as though 'the system' was swallowing her up. But at the same time I was hugely grateful that this most compassionate representative was taking charge. I didn't have to be totally responsible, to shoulder all the burden.

Could we take her up to the hospital? the doctor asks. Quicker than trying to organise an ambulance, we're told. It's agreed we'll go up in Alan and Sue's car. We gather a few things together – pyjamas, flannel, soap, towel, slippers, comb…what does a person need in hospital? We get Mum ready to go – of course we explain what's happening and assume, because it's simpler that way, that she understands. Dad kisses her goodbye – she's been the centre, and the love, of his life for 70 years, and here we are taking her off into the night with little awareness of what this feels like for him. Maybe he already knows, or fears, that she won't come back. As for Mum, her leg was painful so the struggle to get into the car took all her attention. She left in the clothes she happened to be wearing. There was no waving goodbye, no last glance.

Scene 3B: 8.30 pm: Fun and games in Medical Assessment

The doctor's instructions are to go to A&E and hand in his letter. We arrive, grab a wheelchair and push Mum inside to take her part in the human drama that is A&E at night. Couples, youths, anxious family groups, and Mum, in her wheelchair, with no very clear idea where she is. Not that this fazes her: people are a source of endless entertainment for her and there are plenty of people here.

As Mum is to be admitted into hospital, our first destination is the Medical Assessment Unit which shares a Reception Desk with A&E. It's moved from when I came up to Addenbrooke's Hospital with Dad last spring when he had an emergency admission for extreme anaemia. Just over a year ago I had blithely assumed that Mum would be OK on her own while Dad spent a couple of nights in hospital. That's how tough I believed her to be when the reality was that her mind was already breaking.

Not that she'd been so confident she'd be OK. I remember her saying after spending the night on her own: 'I was alright', as though she was relieved and rather pleased with herself. It hadn't occurred to me she wouldn't be OK even though her dementia must have been already present. Another example of taking her at face value.

What could I have been thinking of? I guess the answer is that I could only cope with one of them not being OK at a time. Back last March, Dad was in the limelight, Mum relegated to a minor role. Today, Mum's the star of the show. Dad's at home, offstage, where he is playing out his own drama. I fail to anticipate that one too.

We're asked to wait in A&E till they're ready for her in the Medical Assessment Unit. A somewhat overweight girl is sitting nearby. Fatness is one of Mum's prejudices, commenting on fatness one of her favourite topics. 'Look at that fatty', she says, not loudly but not quietly either: dementia can remove or reduce inhibitions. We try to shush her. 'Look at her!' Mum insists. Alan's wife, Sue, turns the wheelchair away so Mum's looking towards a wall rather than the waiting patients, but Mum isn't having any. 'I'd rather be back there', she says turning her head. Sue relents and turns the wheelchair back. A young black girl with dreadlocks comes in. 'Do you see that hair!' Mum exclaims – we're saved by being called into the Assessment Unit.

We're shown into a cubicle and with difficulty get Mum out of the wheelchair and on to the bed. It's around 9 pm by this time. My abiding memory of the next three hours (we're there till after midnight) is of laughter. No real idea what is going on (because, I guess, she's unable to remember from one moment to the next what she's told), Mum turns everything into a joke. This is her strategy, the one she adopts to cope with the outside world – we haven't seen much of it so far as she hadn't needed it at home. But it's a good one – her laughter is infectious: the doctors and nurses end up laughing too. Asked by an administrator her date of birth, she doesn't know. Asked her age though, she plays to the gallery; acts all coy and giggly, 'I'll whisper it', she says. And she does. '90', she mouths in a moment of clarity.

Examined head to toe

The assessment process seems to be a series of head to toe tests: and the first nurse who comes to start the process is Lynette, short, black, pleasant but not particularly cheery. Though Mum isn't racist, she does belong to that generation and small town background for whom black, or 'coloured' people are still unusual, and therefore may be commented upon. I'm hoping, therefore, that she won't make any remarks on Lynette's blackness. She does show a sliver of surprise and looks over to us for some reaction, but finding none, she accepts Lynette's ministrations. Nevertheless, I find myself chatting brightly, non-stop so as not to leave any gaps for an unfortunate remark to intrude. As Lynette leans over her Mum seems fascinated by her short black wiry hair, but whatever she's thinking, she keeps it to herself.

A junior house doctor called Ruth introduces herself. She's lovely – warm, considerate with a wonderful bedside manner, happy to joke with Mum. In layman's language she explains the assessment procedure, the blood tests and X-rays and efforts to find the source of Mum's infection. They're nothing if not thorough, I'm thinking, listening to Ruth, and wondering how long it will be before the system blunts her youthful kindness and enthusiasm. But just at this moment she's perfect.

Ruth leaves and Sue notices Mum's feet are twitching. 'What's wrong?' 'I need to do a pittle', Mum says, trying to get up off the bed. I get hold of Lynette who goes off to fetch a commode. Mum's very agitated; Lynette seems to be taking a long time. Mum's bolt upright by this time, mustering all her strength to push herself to the end of the bed so she can get to a toilet. 'She won't be long', I say but Mum's eyes are staring straight ahead. 'Fred! Fred!' she calls. But Fred isn't there.

Lynette shows up at last wheeling the commode. Lifting Mum on to it is a challenge as she can't easily follow instructions; her leg is painful and there's not much room in the cubicle. But we manage. She pees, relaxes and we all laugh. She's also, rather conveniently, produced a urine sample.

The tests definitely show an infection but they're still not sure of the source: is it urinary? Chest? Or could it have something to do with that nasty rash that was revealed when Lynette undressed her and put on a hospital gown. It was a shock to see it, so raw and red. Mum has large breasts that have drooped with age, and this was right in the fold. There was some toilet paper covering it where Mum had tried to treat it herself. She'd never mentioned it or showed it to anyone, of course. That was her way, even in dementia. Deal with personal matters personally, that was always her strategy. Telling others only means interference and interference means trouble.

When it seemed there could be no more examining they could possibly do, Lynette comes back to take a mouth and nose swab. The throat swab Mum can accept and dutifully opens her mouth. But a stick up your nose! She laughs at the very idea! And laughs. And laughs. Lynette begins to laugh with her. We all do.

Though it's late at night and we are fading fast, Mum doesn't seem tired. On the contrary, she's perking up and seems to be quite enjoying herself. One of the male nurses has a Mohican haircut which she tut-tuts at but can't keep her eyes off. Ruth reappears to say she's going off duty and that her supervisor, the Registrar, who she tells us is tending a very sick patient at the other end of the hospital, will come and check her findings. Then they'll get Mum on to a ward.

When the Registrar eventually turns up he treats Mum with kindness. 'Kindness' is a word Mum doesn't lose even as her dementia gets worse. She remains aware of being treated with kindness; she remains able to say so. He's black too and as he bends over her, Mum is fascinated by his hair as she was with Lynette's. He organises a final X-ray of her painful leg, after which, at nearly 1 am, she's taken to a ward. Not to F4, the 'care of the elderly ward' where she's 'supposed' to go. They don't have any beds. So she's taken to the Emergency Surgery Short Stay Ward, her bed wheeled through the deserted corridors by two cheery young men.

The nurses get her to bed. She laughs happily as we leave her there. It's a strange place she's come to in the middle of the night but she doesn't seem too worried. I guess when you're mentally confused everywhere is strange.

It's Monday morning already. The Weekend is over, the action now well underway. As the curtain falls for the interval, we three supporting players go out into the night.

Chapter 2
I can't look after her

In the long lead up to our family's Crisis Weekend, Dad had been the one most often centre stage. His physical health had gradually become his major preoccupation and by extension had come to preoccupy me, though interestingly, not Mum. She had probably been mentally living in the past for longer than we realised and therefore saw Dad as still a strong and vigorous man. Dad's mental health had also been an increasing worry – even before the vascular dementia diagnosis he'd had several years of low spirits diagnosed as depression. Mum's robust response had alternated between insisting he must have Alzheimer's and telling him to snap out of it and cheer up.

Against this background of Dad being the one with the health problems, Mum's mental breaking down had not been part of anyone's script. Sure, I knew she got confused, that she had memory problems, but severely demented? That was a big shock. What I didn't yet know was that dementia sufferers can often manage in a familiar environment for a long time, the full extent of their confusion only revealed when they're confronted with a new place. And for Mum Addenbrooke's Hospital was that new place. She'd suddenly become the leading player. All eyes were on her, leaving Dad in the wings sitting forlornly in the dark. Not that I realised his predicament till later.

It was the early hours of Monday morning before Alan and Sue drove back to their home in Stamford leaving me as the main link with the hospital. Of course I'd rung Dad during the evening from the Medical Assessment Unit to tell him Mum was OK reassuring him he could go to bed. We'd also driven by the house in the early hours in case he was still up but the lights were out and we'd assumed he was safely asleep.

Scene 4: Monday 16th July 2007: Care Manager calling

When Dad had been in hospital the year before, I'd assumed Mum would be OK on her own. Similarly with Dad, I took it for granted he would manage. We're a robust family expecting to take care of ourselves. If I'd thought about it, which with so much else going on I didn't, it might have struck me sooner that Dad had never actually been on his own at home, at least not for 40, maybe 50 years. Since Alan and I were born in the later 1940s Mum had scarcely ever been in hospital as an in-patient. Unlike Dad who in old age had two prostate ops, a hip replacement and the recent anaemia episode. Mum had therefore had experience of being alone whereas Dad had none. Till now. At 90 years old with an ageing body and failing mind.

I was surprised, therefore, next morning to get a call from Michelle, who introduced herself as the Care Manager for Mum's temporary ward. I assumed she was calling with news about Mum. But no, it was Dad she was concerned about. She explained that her assistant had rung him earlier and couldn't get any coherent account as to how he was being looked after, or as she put it in the jargon of 'the system', what kind of care he had in place.

At that point in my trial and error efforts to look after Mum and Dad I didn't even know what a Care Manager was. I was only vaguely aware that hospitals have a duty of care and are not supposed to discharge patients into a void but need to check they have some kind of 'care in place' that will ensure vulnerable people are safe in their own homes. Now that Mum was in 'the system', Dad, as the other member of this elderly household to which it was assumed Mum would eventually return, apparently was in 'the system' too.

I liked the sound of Michelle, North American accent, capable and concerned. 'Is your Dad OK?' she asks. 'Oh yes', I say blithely. 'He's been finding it hard to cope with Mum lately. He'll probably be glad of the break'. That's what I said because that's what I assumed without thinking: that Mum's stay in hospital would give Dad a much-needed break from coping with the fallout of her failing mind. So much was he not the centre of my attention, I was somehow assuming he'd been taking care of Mum as her dementia worsened when actually he'd been more of a helpless observer. What was it he'd said? 'I don't know where she sleeps'. Looking back I see I was speaking for myself: I needed a break from taking responsibility and was projecting my emotional exhaustion on to Dad. I was also largely disregarding his vascular dementia, its effects being so much less dramatic than Mum's now very obvious confusion.

Michelle doesn't sound too convinced, however. Care Managers need evidence, not just the optimistic say-so of a relative. For them safety is of paramount concern. Was Dad safe to be left at home alone? Michelle plants doubt in my mind: 'I'll go straight round and find out', I say. 'I'll see how he is and call you back'.

I go round and find Dad curled up into an almost foetal position. He sighs when he sees me. 'Oh dear', he says. A picture of despair. 'What is it, Dad? Are you alright?' 'Oh dear'. He curls up more tightly as I cradle his head in my arms.

'I haven't got a wife'

I didn't see it so clearly then but know now that as Dad lay curled up trying to shut out the world, his despair wasn't principally about the practicalities of his own predicament. It was about loss: 'I haven't got a wife', he said forlornly reflecting perhaps the way his Mary had been drawing away from him and into her own confused world. She'd been the strong one of their partnership, the boss. He'd given her this role freely. 'You'll have to ask your mother', he used to respond to any new proposal. Even recently, when I was trying to organise their household and he knew she was behaving oddly, even then he wouldn't make any decision or agree to any change without her OK. She was the pivot on which he revolved and now she was gone his world had stopped turning.

A few years back in an effort to cheer him up, I'd bought him a journal and suggested he write about his life. He didn't get far but he did record the wonderful day he met Mum, the start of their long love story. 'At 17 I met a 17½ year old blond haired beauty – love at first sight – I was off my food for days. She really was beautiful, very fair. Now, a million years later, I still think the same of her'. I very slowly came to see that when dementia hit both Fred and Mary, he in particular felt the impact most forcibly in his heart, in that special place reserved for his love for his wife.

One reason I didn't understand the depths of his despair was because at this stage, like Michelle, like 'the system' in general, I was operating much more in the realms of practicalities than of feelings. Is Dad OK alone at home? That seemed the urgent question. No, he clearly isn't. What can be done? The 'system' says: put an emergency care package in place. In his case this will mean a visit from two carers from the local emergency team morning and evening. In addition, of course, to me keeping my usual eye on him. Michelle gets on to Social Services and they spring into action via the District Nurses at the GP surgery and the Social Services Care Manager for the elderly for our local area. The kindly carers start coming the very next day, for which I'm extremely grateful.

What we all set aside, me, Michelle, the District Nurses, Social Services, was that practical help, though essential, is just the tip of the iceberg. Deep inside I guess I knew all along that practicalities aren't always the top priority for people who need care. It's helpers and supporters that put physical care at the top of the agenda. Left alone that Sunday night Dad was suddenly exposed to all the emotions and fears that had been swimming beneath the surface. Why on earth hadn't one of us stayed with him? Instead we'd all hared off to the hospital where the main drama seemed to be taking place.

He confides in me one of his deepest fears that 'she won't recognise me', though at first I don't appreciate the profound loss that this would represent. Maybe I don't want to face the possibility that my Mum won't recognise my Dad, or me, or my brother. Rationally of course I do 'know' that stage is likely to come. I know it with my reason, but I don't know it with my heart. Clearly it's not just Dad's feelings and fears that are swimming beneath the surface. My own coping mechanisms are also working overtime.

Maybe it's too soon for me to face such a grim prognostic since I'm only just being forced to recognise how far Mum's dementia has progressed. I still want to believe that somehow it's going to be OK. We'll get Mum home with some extra help and life will return to something like normality. Dad's ahead of me on that one though. He knows this isn't going to happen. He is already grieving.

So while I'm genuinely and unreservedly grateful for the concern and practical help provided by 'the system', and equally grateful for the empathy and kindness I received from the various carers and Care Managers who were involved, I'm also aware that the deeper drama was being played out elsewhere: in my attempts to remain upbeat, to play my role as the strong one who can make everything alright, in Dad's struggles to cope with the new realities that were forcing their way into his life, in our sadness and fears and anxieties as we walked into an unknown future.

A gaping hole where Mary used to be

As it turned out, Mum and Dad's love story had not ended though it was soon to enter a new phase. At this stage, in the absence of Mum, 24 Acrefield Drive becomes a gloomy place in spite of the kindly carers who come in morning and evening to jolly Dad along and make him tea and toast. Dad rattles about. Or shuts out the pain with sleep. Mum used to worry about the amount he was sleeping, constantly nudging him awake when he tried to drop off. Now there is no-one to nag him.

I go round often but have to steel myself each time: 'Hi, Dad, how's it going?' It seems my natural impulse is to be upbeat. 'Terrible', he says, resolutely refusing to pretend he is anything other than desolate. That's something I'd noticed these latter years, his determination to give up on life. Stronger than apathy, a kind of stubbornness, digging in, repeating the mantra: 'I'm old. My life is over', defying all our efforts to draw him back in.

Attempts at conversation now produce complaints: about the cost of the newspapers that are still delivered daily though he doesn't want them – it was Mum who always wanted a paper. Even now if she sees one lying about she reads the headlines aloud. 'Shall I cancel them for you?' Ever practical, if there's a problem, I offer a solution.

Then there's the front window curtains: they had started to come away from the pole at one end and Dad had coped with this by opening and closing them very gingerly. But now the carers come in and brightly fling them open as they say 'Good morning'. As a result they now droop crazily from one corner. 'Hateful' is how Dad describes it: that must be how it feels to him, reinforcing the way life is falling apart. Lorraine, one of the District Nurses, calls round to see how he is managing: he tells her to call me ('she does the talking', he says). 'All he did was complain about the curtains', Lorraine reports.

Alan and Sue take him up to visit Mum several times, and they get him a hair cut. But none of this makes any impact on his despair. How could it? His life is changed beyond recognition. He was the only one who really knew what a struggle the last months had been; he must have realised they couldn't carry on that way though he hadn't said so. He was the only one too who knew how his own mind was deteriorating. And how his wife, who'd looked after him for all his adult life, had wandered off into her own crazy world. He must have been submerged in a sea of fears none of us had properly understood.

Dad adrift, Mum afloat

Meanwhile, on her 'temporary' ward that began to seem permanent as each new day they tried and failed to 'find her a bed' on the elderly ward, Mum is having her own adventures. On one of my visits, a couple of days after her admission, I'm surprised to find her moved from the original six-bed ward into a room of her own. Notices at the door warn visitors to wash our hands before entering and on leaving. She's contracted C. difficile, I'm told. 'We don't know if she got it in the community or in hospital', they say. Though I'd heard of MRSA, I didn't know at that time that C.difficile was also rife in hospitals; the adverse publicity hadn't yet hit the headlines. So I didn't say: 'Surely it's more likely she caught it here', though that's what I thought.

I'm glad I didn't know then that C.difficile can be dangerous and occasionally fatal in old people. Though actually Mum seems remarkably perky: I conclude she must have a fairly mild attack. I piece together the story of her having a nasty burst of diarrhoea which I guess went all over the place. Mum tells me her version: a man in a smart suit, she tells me in shocked tones, came in and made a shitty mess and acted as though it was quite normal. People with confused minds, as I understand it, often imagine stories to try and make sense of what they can no longer understand.

'Confabulation' I later learn this is called. I guess this shitty man in his smart suit was one of Mum's confabulations.

Though I would never have wished her to have the C. difficile infection, the fact that it gave her a room of her own, with an internal window through which she could observe what was going on and passing staff would wave to her, was a definite plus. Mum's pretty robust in spite of her advanced years – her body managed to deal with C.difficile more easily than with her failing memory. She had her own loo in this private room though she'd sometimes go in and forget how to get out. She was treated kindly on this ward, her smiles and laughter making her popular. I was treated kindly too, catering staff sometimes pressing quite tasty puds on me rather than waste them, patient appetites on the Emergency Surgery Short Stay Ward unsurprisingly being small.

Through various conversations with Michelle I also came to see that 'the system' was testing her for two very different sorts of outcome. As one might expect, there were medical tests: these were looking pretty good. In fact I was given to understand that once the C.difficile infection cleared she'd be 'medically fit for discharge'. Medically fit, perhaps, but not ready for discharge, since this required leaving hospital for a setting that was safe for her, given her age and her dementia. Without more care in place, her own home was not at present considered safe enough.

Tests and assessments

The other kinds of tests and assessments were therefore in the domain of 'care' to evaluate what Mum could do for herself, and where she would need help. For these tests she saw various physio and occupational therapists. One told me Mum had said she lived in Middlesbrough, the Teesside town where she'd worked as a young woman, a comptometer operator for Dorman Long, the steel manufacturers who diversified into bridges and built among others the Tyne Bridge and the Sydney Harbour Bridge. She'd also said that she and my Dad didn't have any children yet. Though eventually I got used to it, this was the first time I became fully aware of the way dementia can allow you to operate in different time zones, the present and a long-gone past, at the same time.

Another day, as part of the hospital's testing of Mum's capabilities, a friendly young Occupational Therapist took her down to one of their kitchens to assess whether she was capable of putting a ready-made frozen meal into the oven for the correct length of time. I knew Mum would fail but didn't say so assuming 'the system' needed to establish this for itself.

It was a time I happened to be visiting so I go down too. Mum loves being pushed around the corridors and in and out of the lifts. So much to see, so many notices to read aloud! As often happened with her at that time, what starts out as a serious exercise ends in hysterical laughter. I try to sit in the background but Mum keeps bringing me in: 'you do it', she says when the OT asks her to read the 'time in the oven' information from the label on the frozen meal (which, I notice, is exactly the same type – Wiltshire Farm Foods – as she and Dad have been eating for months if not years). 'Don't ask me to do it', I say. 'We're supposed to be seeing if you can do it'.

She can't, of course, but is very good at using diversionary tactics to disguise the fact. Disguise is an important skill developed by dementia sufferers particularly in the early to mid stages where concealing their condition is still possible. Mum's tactics include asking for a drink, reading the full list of ingredients out loud, trying to delegate the task to me. What intrigues me is that, though I faithfully ordered these frozen meals online, and she has eaten one of these every day for many, many months, she doesn't appear to recognise them at all. Like so much of her everyday life they have simply melted away.

With her short and medium term memory almost wiped out (for instance, though she has lived in Cambridge for the past 30 years, the notion 'Cambridge' seems to have entirely gone), she still has earlier memories reasonably intact. And so she searches around these earlier memories, moving around within these long-gone times: at one moment she can be a recently-married woman who hasn't any children yet. At others she can be even younger, unmarried, Fred her boyfriend whom she suddenly realises she hasn't seen for a while and worries he might marry someone else. 'Tell him Mary says not to marry anyone else', she says to me, her 60+ year old daughter. 'I will', I say. And then that memory, and that worry too, slip away.

Scene 5: 24th July: 'I can't look after her'

There was though one really striking thing I'd noticed and that was that in all her time in Addenbrooke's Hospital, Mum had made no reference to home. None whatsoever. She'd never once asked when she'd go home or how Dad was getting on at home. Strange that, I thought at first, considering that she'd barely set foot outside the house for over a year. I noted it but didn't immediately conclude she'd forgotten her home completely. For me that was a leap of imagination too far, that on walking out of her door barely ten days before, her home of 30 years had been wiped from her memory.

At this stage in my own thinking I still assume Mum will go back home when she's discharged and 'the system' will help in getting more 'care in place' for us, Mum and Dad and me, to continue muddling along. Actually I don't know that my thought processes were that coherent. Certainly I felt very responsible for making sure Mum and Dad were alright, but with all these new developments I didn't have a clear picture of our future.

On 24th July, around ten days after Mum's admission to the hospital, I learn that a bed has finally been found for her on F4, one of the elderly wards. She's now medically fit for discharge, but not 'socially fit' as she's liable to wander at night. Sadly, in moving wards, we move out of Michelle's capable hands. F4 will have a different Care Manager. However, before we lose her, she gives me a last call.

It was a sunny late July day and I was visiting Dad. I went into the garden to talk. Dad was more perky that day; he had the TV on when I arrived (a good sign) and was putting his Wiltshire Farm Foods lunch in the microwave. With his new hair cut he looked decidedly smarter. I tell him Mum's much better and can come home soon, but he seems to be shaking his head. 'I can't look after her. I've got enough on looking after myself'. He'd already said that the week before. And here he was saying it again.

Michelle doesn't seem to feel Mum can come home either. 'If I was hearing from your Dad 'I want her at home at all costs, I'll do my best to look after her as long as I can', then we'd take a different view. But that's not the message I'm hearing'. She was right. It wasn't the message I was hearing either.

Dad was the only one who knew from the inside how his vascular dementia was affecting him. He knew much better than me what he was capable of and what he wasn't. 'I've got enough on looking after myself' was the message he'd been trying to get over to us, but couldn't clearly explain precisely because his own dementia impaired his ability to find words. The very fact that he couldn't explain what he felt should have alerted me that his mind was worse than I thought. He was right: he wasn't a fit carer for a wife with significant dementia.

Michelle spells out the blunt truth. A so-called full care package might be four visits a day from carers, each visit around half an hour: 'That leaves 22 hours every day when he would be responsible'. Around two thirds of which he'd be asleep, I add to myself. Put that way I wondered how, as a society, we could possibly think that sending in carers for short bursts a few times a day constitutes care. A pragmatic people, we put the emphasis on the physical: 30 minutes is enough, I guess, to get someone up and help them get washed. And then what? Leave them on their own till the next hurried visit. Fine, if they have all the their faculties and still have a life of sorts. But if they're frail, forgetful and very much on the fringes of our full-on society? Are we deluding ourselves on a large scale?

I feel I'm in a drama where I don't know the script. Aren't old people supposed to be better off staying in their own homes? Isn't that the accepted wisdom? Yet if Dad can't look after Mum even with carers coming in several times a day…

Mum and Dad had managed well, it was becoming clear, staying independent into very old age largely because they were two; they kept each other going even in the hard times, when Mum was repeating herself endlessly, and Dad was depressed. 'Always look on the bright side', Mum would recite, 'and if you can see no bright. Set to work on the dark side and polish with all your might'. But now dementia was worming its way into their lives, cracking open this long partnership. As Dad could see no alternative but to let her go, we were witnessing the disintegration of this couple as a self-sustaining unit.

'Should I be looking for a care home?'

'Should I be looking for a care home?' I hear myself asking. 'You could start some preliminary looking', Michelle replies. Along with everything else I hadn't known was another new fact: hospitals often take on responsibility for finding residential care and have a department dedicated to the search. I began to understand what is meant by 'bed blocking': patients, like Mum, I guess, who are medically fit for discharge but for whom 'the system' has not yet managed to find suitable care arrangements. Not that she ended up 'blocking' a bed on F4 for much more than a week, as it turned out.

From the hospital point of view, I realised, our situation was commonplace: old lady no longer able to live at home needs residential care. Michelle was kind and encouraging in assuring me they wouldn't force us to decide Mum's fate quickly. I had another worry anyway: my own life was still struggling to assert itself and in early August I was due to go on a yoga course in France. Worn out and needing a break, I desperately wanted to go. I wanted to be selfish, to lose myself in the French countryside, to focus on me rather than my parents for a while. One of the many discoveries I made about myself during this time was the strength of my instinct for self-protection. I was capable of helping, and helping, and helping – but then, at a certain point, I'd know it was time to look after me. I should go, Michelle, said, giving me to understand without actually promising anything they wouldn't discharge her while I was away.

I went inside from the garden trying to get my mind round the notion that Mum wouldn't be coming home, that she would be going into a care home. It felt like a foreign language. Charmain, our wonderful helper from Crossroads, turned up for her usual Tuesday afternoon slot. We talked again to Dad about Mum coming home. Charmain too could see that he couldn't handle having her back.

And so the drama moved inexorably on. Mum duly moved to F4. The hospital continued to assess her capabilities. I surveyed our options. Me becoming a full-time carer? Hardly fair on Terry. Or me – my instinct for self-protection said a definite no. Employ a live-in carer? Possible but their house was so tiny this didn't feel like a solution. There was no real alternative – I was going to have to start looking at care homes. Mum remained the centre of attention for a while longer. Dad settled deeper and more dejectedly into his role as 'the one left behind.'

'It's hard', I remember saying to Michelle in our last conversation. 'It'll get harder', she replied.

Chapter 3

Nine days to change two lives

Unaware of the family drama of which she was unwittingly the star, Mum cheerfully moved to her new ward on 24th July. Her temporary ward, the Emergency Surgery Short Stay Ward had been a tight, closed world. Entry by intercom. Small number of beds. An air of quiet urgency. Even the name had a life and death tinge to it. Visiting Mum on F4, one of the hospital's two 'elderly' wards, was a whole different experience. The approach was via a long corridor with information panels about Alzheimer's on one of the side walls. Odd, when you think about it, that the hospital should highlight the mental like this when in practice medics regularly ignore an elderly patient's dementia and focus firmly on the physical.

As you got closer you heard the noise – a thin wailing, a constant moaning cry which you might think, if you were feeling fanciful, expressed the desperate sadness of human disintegration and decay. In a way it was: the plaintive cries came from a lady called Maisie who, I was told, had lived happily enough in her own home with moderate dementia until one day something happened. No-one knew precisely what but she'd been found unconscious on the floor. After extensive tests the best hypothesis was she'd had a serious heart attack, but whatever the cause, Maisie was left in a sad state, barely opening her eyes, the stimulation of lights and people seeming to frighten her. She moaned constantly, but for all anyone knew she was desperately trying to make herself understood. With true devotion her son and daughter-in-law spent many hours coaxing her to drink liquids. The sound of her distress was haunting, poignant.

The first time I visited F4 I bumped into Mum outside the ward – one of the nurses was bringing her back from the other elderly ward, G4, on to which she'd wandered. Unlike most of the other patients who seemed to stick to their beds, Mum was a tireless wanderer, curious about everything, reading aloud all the notices she saw yet oblivious to their meaning. Her bed was in the far corner of the endmost six-bed bay, just past the nurses station and close to Maisie's room, the moaning getting louder as you approached. I was pleased Mum had a bed next to a window even though, as her conversation showed, she had no real idea what she was looking out at.

The other wanderer on the ward at the time was Irene, a silent lady who would appear from nowhere and sit at the end of Mum's bed for a while. Or sometimes they'd wander together in their matching flowered hospital nightgowns. 'We call them the gruesome twosome', one of the nurses joked to me when I'd become a more familiar visitor. Oddly enough, to have a nickname felt positive: they were noticed, they got attention; most important, they were treated kindly.

Back out in the world

Back out in the world, still shell-shocked by the looming change in our lives, I am starting to look for a residential care home. One relief is that Mum appears able to settle anywhere. Provided she sees plenty of smiles around her, she seems quite happy. This proviso is important. Her physical setting doesn't seem to matter much to her. But the emotional temperature does. Dourness unsettles her. Maybe that's why she smiles and laughs such a lot. To generate the warmth around her that, instinctively, she knows she needs. I was already learning a most important lesson about dementia: that emotions and feelings can remain largely intact when memory and rational thoughts fail.

I guess life does puzzle her though. 'Where do you go when you're not here?' she asks one day. 'Home', I say. 'I have a home to go to'. 'Do you?' she says in surprise. 'Where is it?' Because I don't know any better at this point, I try to talk to her about the future, about what will happen when she's discharged from hospital. What these conversations lay bare is that she doesn't know she's in hospital at all. A side of me can't believe she genuinely doesn't know. 'You're in hospital', I tell her to establish a starting point for the discussion. 'Am I?' It's that surprised tone again. As though she's humouring me and doesn't really believe a word I say. I'm fascinated by how you can be so obviously in hospital, looking around curiously at everything, and yet not know it. 'What do you think these beds and nurses and doctors are doing here if it's not a hospital?' A pointless question. Mum simply ignores it.

I realise I'm as curious as my mother. Only in my case I'm curious about her, about what goes on in the mind of a sufferer from Alzheimer's-type dementia like Mum. I want to know more about what it's like from the inside. I've seen that people with her kind of dementia can be somewhere without necessarily knowing where it is. What I'd like to know is whether they wonder 'Where am I?' or just accept that they are where they are. Looked at from the outside, when Mum was in hospital it seemed that she had no 'big picture' knowledge of where she was: maybe she'd forgotten the meaning of the word 'hospital', or maybe the whole idea of 'hospital' had disappeared. Yet at the same time, she could still, living as she was in an eternal present, be fascinated by details, by the myriad of tiny hospital happenings immediately around her. As she became stronger physically, so her curiosity grew: she was determined to find out what every noise, bump or swaying of the curtain signified.

Still intact too was that unfortunate tendency we'd seen in A&E, when she was being admitted, to make personal remarks. Dementia definitely diminishes inhibitions. The woman in the next bed had a relative, maybe her daughter, who was somewhat overweight. 'Look at that fatty', Mum would say wanting my agreement as I desperately tried to change the subject hoping no-one had heard. Another patient had huge legs which Mum kept pointing out. Just as she pointed out ceiling fittings and curtain rails. Everything fascinates her and she keeps asking questions. But without a 'big picture' to help her make sense of the world, she immediately forgets the answers.

Entering uncharted territory

In starting to look for a care home I enter what is for me uncharted territory. I have no map, not even a tentative plan. True, during our Crisis Weekend the 'awful doctor' had planted a seed but it had barely grown at all. Until these last weeks I'd never seriously thought either of my parents would go into a home.

Having simply assumed we'd cope somehow I'd never questioned the accepted wisdoms about care that I had unwittingly internalised, in particular the assumption that old people are always better off staying in their own homes. With hindsight, one reason I'd unquestioningly accepted this assumption was that I myself would rather stay in my own home. Wouldn't we all? At least that's what we think when, like me, we're fit, healthy and fully able to take care of ourselves. Those who make policies for elderly folk, which are based on assumptions about how they should best live, are themselves for the most part as fit and healthy and unlike those for whom they are deciding as I am. They have little real idea how things might change if they became frail, lonely or lost their minds. I have little idea how my views might change if I became frail, lonely or developed Alzheimer's.

Whatever the accepted wisdom, however, our reality was that Mum's dementia had advanced to the stage where she couldn't go back to her own home – a home she'd already forgotten – even with a 'full care package'. For the 22 hours when carers were not there, Dad couldn't keep an eye on her as much as she'd need. He slept soundly at night and intermittently for much of the day and would not notice her wandering. And though I was willing to prop them up as much or more than before, I wasn't prepared to become a 24 hour carer. That I knew for certain. I had my own family and my own life. We therefore had no option but to find a residential home.

The hospital would have helped – I was given the name of the hospital's 'care home organiser' but she just happened to be on holiday. So I started the search alone. My tools: a directory of Cambridgeshire services for old people, including care homes, and the internet.

I was also aware that care homes are expensive and that if you had savings of a little over £20,000 then you had to pay the lot. Not long before I'd been through my parents' savings and organised all the paperwork (work that Dad used to do but had let slip accentuating his anxiety about things falling apart). So I knew the approximate score. In income terms Dad had a very modest occupational pension and a state pension. Mum had a tiny 'married woman's pension' and no more income in her own name. They both had Attendance Allowance at the basic not full rate at that point. In no way, therefore, were they rich. But they were both 90 and over the past few years had spent very little such that their spare income had accumulated each month. This, together with their life savings – they belonged to the generation for whom saving came naturally – pushed them well over the £20,000 or so limit. That was true for each of them even after splitting their finances, which I did on the advice of the hospital's 'care home organiser' whom I eventually caught up with.

I could see therefore from the outset that this was going to be an expensive business. One of the plus sides, however, (maybe the only one!) was that falling into the 'fully self-funding' category gave us free rein. No waiting for local authorities to agree anything. If I found a home I liked, and they could take her, we could write them a cheque and Mum could move in. Just like that.

The search begins

The directory of old people's services listed homes in and around the city. Eight of them said they accepted residents with dementia. I used the internet to check the Commission for Social Care Inspection (CSCI) report for each of the possible candidate homes. (The CSCI has now, sadly, been replaced by the Care Quality Commission whose reports focus on compliance and are less easy to use in choosing a home). The idea of these reports was to bestow occasional praise but mainly to highlight shortcomings in care homes so these could be rectified. Scanning through them was a depressing business as it brought out the main negatives I was quickly coming to realise are often found in care homes for old people (smell of urine, high staff turnover, insufficient staff training…).

Before I got too depressed I decided to visit a home to see what they were really like. I identified one less than ten minutes walk from our house at the end of a quiet side street. How convenient, I thought. I could pop round to see Mum any time. The report wasn't too bad, though they did pick out as a negative the smell of urine in the lounges on the dementia floor. It was also dawning on me that a home that said they accepted residents with dementia probably didn't have them wandering about with the other residents. There would be separation. Locked doors.

On the scent

I rang to arrange an appointment. The response was pleasant enough if a little casual: come when you like, someone will show you round. And so I did, that same afternoon. Rang the bell, explained my mission. The manager wasn't there but the young woman who showed me round was very obliging: 'It's a nice home', she enthused as we went into the downstairs residents' lounge which felt small and crowded.

When I repeated that my mother had dementia, she took me upstairs to the 'dementia floor'. The corridor was light and bright with windows all down one side. The residents' rooms had pictures on the door as well as their names. Bathrooms had big hoists which gave a Heath Robinsonish impression until I realised I was being initiated into the realities of old age – how else other than hoisting were you going to get stiff-limbed old people with weakened muscles into the bath? I made a mental note to keep up my yoga so my own limbs stayed supple and my muscles strong.

The dining room on the dementia floor was OK. But the two lounges. The smell of urine was all-pervasive in both. Did my guide not smell it? Did the residents sitting there not smell it? No, I couldn't possibly bring my mother here, she who had always had a very sharp sense of smell. No, definitely not. They had a respite care room which my guide showed me: 'Bring her in here for a trial week. That's the best way. She'll like it. It's a nice home'. I assured her I'd think about it and left as soon as I decently could.

Gloom descended. I'd experienced the reality behind these CSCI reports and it wasn't pretty. I was afraid all the homes in the city were going to be smelly and depressing. Or out-of-reach expensive. As far as I could understand the system, if I found somewhere so hugely expensive that Mum's money ran out quickly, the local authority could require her to move somewhere cheaper before they would pay.

Back to the drawing board

Back to the drawing board: I found two small homes with quite good reports whose directory entry claimed they took residents with dementia. Could I visit? Yes, they said. Er, rather no, they backtracked when I mentioned dementia. What I understood was that if one of their existing residents became more confused they probably wouldn't throw them out, but they wouldn't take people who clearly had dementia from the start.

Dementia, I was coming to see, was a grey area (pun not intended) when it came to care homes. If you have mild dementia (perhaps you're a bit confused but easy to look after maybe with some physical disability so you can't wander far on your own), then somehow your impaired mental state doesn't really count. The home will treat your less than sharp mental capacities as a natural part of ageing.

But if you are more obviously confused or wander and are not easily contained, that does count as dementia. That was how it was starting to look to me. Such an odd state of affairs is made possible in part precisely because, until recently at least, two out of three dementia sufferers have not been formally diagnosed, and of course Mum was one of the two. I began to wonder if I'd been wrong to mention her dementia at all: perhaps I should have tried to get her into one of these nice, small homes and see if anyone noticed. The only flaw in this plan was that they almost certainly would!

A sigh of relief

Despair was looming. I simply couldn't bear Mum to be in a home that was just tolerable. A neighbour's wife had developed Alzheimer's and was in a home on the other side of town. But the CSCI report for that one was not encouraging. Another home's report mentioned that smell of urine again. There were only two left on my list, both on my side of town, reports not too bad.

I phoned one and the number was engaged; I phoned the other and was met with a kindly welcoming response. Can I come and visit? Of course. Today?

The home was a modern U-shaped brick building with a small car park and a garden in the centre. The sun was shining and an old lady was dozing in an armchair in the sun-bathed lobby. I could visit here, I thought immediately. There was an openness, lots of glass and light. I could breathe.

The administrator took me round first showing me upstairs, the 'ordinary residential' section: light, bright lounge/dining room, two wings of residents' rooms. Then the Green Unit, the Elderly Mentally Infirm (EMI) Unit as it was then called, on the ground floor, along a short corridor from the entrance, through a door with a security code. My guide stressed that EMI residents could go out of the Unit, but they needed to be accompanied. The code was for their own safety and security so they didn't wander off.

'We've got a room free at the moment', she said showing me room 5. 'They don't come up very often but we've had a couple of deaths recently'. The room is plain but clean and has its own bathroom. Out of the window is a tree and I notice a squirrel: he seems like a messenger. Mum used to open the curtains at home and, on the trees at the back of their house, she'd often see squirrels, and she'd want to tell us about them but she couldn't always remember the word: 'Them with the tails', she'd say. Squirrels. 'Yes, squirrels'.

We go into the lounge: old ladies are sitting around in armchairs. One is having her nails painted, talking quite articulately about the colour. The lounge is light and bright with a dining area at one end, windows all around and their own little garden through French doors. Home for eleven residents, this Unit; only ten at present. 'I like the sound of your mother', my guide says. She gives me the costs of the home – expensive but not out-of-reach: what I'd come to expect. I should fill out an application form, she says, to declare an interest and get into their admin system. No obligation at this stage.

I hear myself agreeing to fill in the form, saying I'm interested in the free room. I'm not a decisive person normally, but here I was making a decision. Lots of light. No smell of urine. I could come here, I felt, without my heart sinking with sorrow. And so, without consulting anyone else at this stage, I declared a strong interest in room 5, thereby setting in motion the next step: the home making their own assessment of Mum. This was Thursday, 26th July, two days after my search began. Later that day I had a call from one of the assistant managers saying they'd come to the hospital and assess Mum on Monday morning. Things were suddenly moving fast.

I went round to see Dad. 'I've found a nice home for Mum', I tell him. 'It's just round the corner'. She can come home from time to time once she's settled in: that was the picture I painted since, in spite of all the evidence to the contrary, I still didn't really believe that she could already have forgotten her home of 30 years. Dad seemed pleased. We talked about money and Dad accepted what it would cost – somewhat to my surprise as he'd often been agitated about money. Perhaps it was my confident assurance that the money side would be OK. It was too, I think, the start of his abdicating financial responsibility and handing it completely to me. He made one last comment a couple of days later about Mum going into 'this place that would bankrupt him'. And that was largely it. Money slipped from his consciousness as a problem.

Final hurdles

Back on the ward, Mum continues to wander. One day I visit and find her in a yellow dressing gown I've never seen before ensconced in the side room occupied by Maisie, the lady in distress. I spot her standing at the end of Maisie's bed; she sees me but is more interested in Maisie's moaning and her son and daughter-in-law's efforts to feed her. Mum has told them her name is Maddie.

Her curiosity is at full throttle as she stares at Maisie who is moaning continuously, eyes tight shut. Her relatives are trying to soothe her. After a while Mum tries to help: 'Belt up!' she says. Maisie's relatives laugh. But it doesn't work. Her son tells me about another time when Mum was in there, with Irene too this time, and they finally got Maisie quiet. Then she started up again. 'Oh bugger!' said Mum.

The days hurry by to Mum's assessment by the home. A habitual worrier, I find myself fretting that something will go wrong. Now that I've found a home I like I'm terrified my solution will be snatched away. But it isn't. The assessment is straightforward, a matter of going through with Mum the questions I've already answered on the form. Mum looks well, and she leaves much of the talking to me, coming in with the odd left field comment about the view out of the window. Of course I explain who these two young assistant managers are, as they do themselves, but I have a strong feeling that Mum has no real idea what's going on, though she puts up a decent show.

The only possible stumbling block to getting her out of hospital and into the home by the end of the week is her GP who has to fill in a report on her health. If the paperwork can be completed I can get her settled in and then go on my yoga course leaving her and Dad in brother Alan's hands for ten days or so. One of the assistant managers says she'll drop the form in to the GP surgery on her way back to the home and ask for it back by the next day. Once they have the GP report they will make us an offer of the place and we can go ahead. But Tuesday passes and nothing happens.

On Wednesday morning the GP surgery say they will take a week: ironic really that they should be the ones to stand in the way since they have taken no interest in Mum and her dementia and have seen very little of her over the past few years. Luckily the home decide that, since Mum has been in hospital and medically examined thoroughly there, they can make an offer before getting the GP report – which will then act as a confirmation. After all, the home does have a three month trial period.

That very day they offer her a place. Hooray! I go in and complete some paperwork, get a cheque from my father for the first month (this is before I visit Mum and Dad's bank and arrange to split their cash assets and register my Power of Attorney with them), ring my brother and check he will come over next day and help with the move. I also have a look at the room again to assess what we need to bring in: bedside table, chest of drawers, some photos and knick-knacks.

I can't quite believe what's happening. It's all been so fast. I count the days. From that phone call with Michelle in the sunshine when we agreed Dad didn't seem able to cope with Mum coming back, to her moving into residential care has only been nine days. Nine days to change a whole mindset, a whole way of life.

'I love you'

At this point I am living between the hospital and Dad at home. And whereas Mum is cheerful, Dad is not. A couple of days before Mum's move I call round and see him sitting forlornly in his chair. He has two carers morning and evening and today he's also had Charmain from Crossroads. Her notes say he's missing Mum. 'Do you want to come up to the hospital with me?' It's a beautiful summer evening: I sort out parking and grab a stray wheelchair for Dad. It's light enough to push but not so easy to steer – I nearly crush his feet as I aim inexpertly for the door of the hospital lift.

We arrive at the foot of Mum's bed and her face lights up. Dad doesn't say much but, ever the romantic, wants to hold her hand. After a short while she takes her hand away. Then he wants to kiss her: 'You're embarrassing me', she says looking around, a realist to his romantic – another illustration of the way dementia destroys mental processes but leaves lots of emotions intact. 'I love you', he says and she says she loves him too but her attention soon wanders to other things: that's the sad side of their continuing love story. He wants to dwell on the only strong feeling he has left, the only thing he continues to care about: his love for her. But she has a world of light fittings and billowing curtains to explore.

After continuing to tell Mum he loves her, Dad is ready to leave. As we make to go, Mum gets up from her bed and goes over to the patient in the bed opposite: it's that insatiable curiosity about what's going on around her again. Then she realises we're leaving: 'What and leave me on my own?' she says. A moment or two later, however, her concern is forgotten. That will be the pattern from now on – pleased to see us but soon forgetting our visit.

Scene 6: Thursday 2nd August: Mum moves in

Mum left home 'for a few days' on 15th July and never went back. That in itself was a big surprise. But much more amazing to me was the way that, once out of that door, she never mentioned home, not even once. Not a word. Those 30 years in Acrefield Drive, Cambridge had simply melted away. When I think about that evening she left, it moves me to remember how this was an ending though we didn't know it. That Mum didn't look back to say goodbye to the home she'd loved brings tears to my eyes even now. I do so wish she had.

On 2nd August she has a new care home address but not only has she forgotten her Acrefield address, she never learns her new one. As her dementia progresses she becomes more and more hazy about where exactly she lives.

As we move her in, Alan and I can't quite believe what's happening. He keeps saying what a big leap it is from muddling along at home to the Elderly Mentally Infirm Unit of a care home. At this stage it feels as though we are putting her in with people who are much worse mentally than she is: but we are bound to think that. Actually some of them are probably less confused than her. She clearly has what I guess by now is at least moderate dementia: it's not mild any more. Maybe with stimulation it will stabilise: for contrary to the popular belief that staying in your own home is always best, Mum will get much more of the stimulation she loves in her new home than she did in those last years living with Dad, who was much of the time asleep or silent.

Singing in the rain

We pick Mum up from the hospital late morning on the 2nd August, the Thursday of that week. They're changing the mattress in her room and it's not quite ready so we sit and wait in the entrance lounge. A small family group. Me, my Mum and my brother. He is doing a show in September and has a small singing part. It's 'Singing in the Rain'. He begins to sing softly: 'Singing in the rain'. Mum joins in – she loves singing. She wants us to carry on so I join in too: a little family island 'singing in the rain' as life swirls on around us.

Mum is also trying to figure out what she's doing here. At one moment she looks at me and says something like: 'Now I understand what you've been saying'. And I wonder if it has finally sunk in that she's going into a home. But no, like everything else it passes. She seems most concerned that this may be a place of employment: she wants to make it clear she can't work any more. She's always been a worker, felt she had lots of jobs to do even in her dementia. In latter times, she'd taken to showing us job adverts as though she or one of us might want to apply. Perhaps, when she was in hospital, she realised she couldn't work any more. That side of life was finished. She needed to be looked after.

Eventually the room is ready: we sit Mum in her armchair which she accepts. The carers on duty are kind and suggest we bring her down to the dining room in a short while. They've kept a place for her. Three ladies are already sitting down at her table for lunch – I'll get to know them well over the coming months. Mum says how tired she is and sits down in the vacant place. The lady opposite seems normal enough and says she'll look after Mum.

We've brought some knick-knacks, photos, a side table, lamp and a few other things so we disappear to organise the room, then go back to check: she seems quite happy. As in hospital, if people are being nice to her, and nice to each other around her, then she feels secure and OK. I just hope her dementia continues in this benign way and doesn't morph into something tougher and sadder.

We go off to what is no longer Mum and Dad's, but in these nine days has become only Dad's, to get a chest of drawers, the one from beside her bed. This means emptying four drawers of what looks like mostly rubbish: it seems that over the past few years Mum never threw anything away. When she finished one lot of thyroid pills, she kept the box. And every other container. And every receipt for every shop she ever went into. We are going to find more of this, much, much more a few months later when we come to sorting the house.

By the time we get back Mum is sitting with the other residents in an armchair: they've had a sing-along, and Mum has been singing along. She doesn't seem to mind when we leave.

I go back to Dad at the end of the day to sort his pills into 'dosset boxes' for the time I'm away. It's time for me to withdraw, leave him to his life and re-enter my own for a while. I'm not sure what he makes of the massive change his and Mum's lives have undergone over these nine days since he made it clear he couldn't look after her at home. He and Mum now have different addresses after 68 years of living together. Different bank accounts after 68 years of being joint. For a while at least they will develop different daily rhythms and routines.

I write in big letters what I'm doing (going to France) and that Alan will be in charge. 'What's happening in France?' he asks and

I tell him about the yoga course. Maybe he even tells me to have a good time. With Mum installed and Dad's carers still coming night and morning, with Alan in charge, and my partner, Terry, available as backup, I finally feel I can leave. With a big sigh of relief, on the tenth day, Friday 3rd August, I make my getaway.

Chapter 4

Fighting mirrors

Dad reclaims centre stage

When Mum went into hospital, Dad became 'the one left behind'. Temporarily we thought. Now she was settling in to the care home, he was once again 'left behind'. But this time, with very little warning, his living alone was permanent. It was 'what he wanted' only in the most literal sense. Yes, he was the one who'd said he couldn't have Mum back. But he hadn't said this was because he wanted to live on his own.

We – me, my brother, Social Services – still thought that with extra help in the form of his own tailored 'care package', he'd manage. What was the alternative? Him going in to a home as well? That 'accepted wisdom' that old people are always better off staying in their own homes kicked in again. No, that couldn't be the right solution. Unlike Mum he did know where he was. Surely he wouldn't want to go into residential care when he could remain in the comfortable familiarity of his own home. Even if it was minus his wife.

His mental deterioration which Dr Dening had, as a best guess, assumed was a vascular dementia (Could he be wrong? we still asked ourselves) seemed slower and more selective in its effects than Mum's Alzheimer's-style dementia. His mind had begun to slur, that's for sure; his decision-making powers had deteriorated and his motivation dulled. But he remained aware of his surroundings; he knew where he was, knew he didn't want to be there but didn't know where else he'd rather be. He'd lost interest in life but still had to get through every day; he couldn't readily find words so couldn't easily share his feelings. He seemed ready to die yet afraid of dying.

Getting extra help for Dad was the domain of the Care Manager for the Elderly for our area. She'd be coming round for a meeting to draw up a permanent care plan for Dad as soon as I was back from my yoga course in France. In the meantime she'd agreed that while I was away the emergency care package would continue. As a further safeguard, I'd also organised an emergency alarm for Dad, one of those press button pendants you wear round your neck to call for help. We had a key safe fitted beside the front door allowing those who knew the code to get in in an emergency, a system that Dad thwarted to start with by bolting the door from the inside at night such that anyone using the key couldn't get in. It wasn't easy to explain that he should leave the door unbolted, thus feeling less secure at night, in order to be more secure 'in case something happened'.

Dreams and hallucinations

Left on his own, however, Dad's behaviour soon challenged our assumption that he could live alone even with extra help. He began to have vivid dreams, or possibly hallucinations, I couldn't be sure: of chairs and tables and especially mirrors coming to life and hitting him. Fighting with these mirrors, he said, felt like going ten rounds with Mike Tyson.

We shouldn't have been surprised his dream life was disturbed considering the massive change his life had undergone. His other half, his 'blond haired beauty', his beloved Mary who had nagged him and annoyed him in her later years but ultimately kept him afloat, was missing. If Mum had died we would have recognised the huge impact of their separation. But because she was still very much in the world, albeit in a different place, we did not understand at first just how violently Dad's world had imploded.

Added to this was a small flaw in the overall plan for keeping an eye on Dad while I was away on my yoga course. Actually quite a big flaw though we'd glossed over it. My brother Alan, again due to a booking made long ago, was himself going away on the Thursday and I wasn't due back till the following Monday. A gap of four days but neither of us wanted to change our plans. Looking back it shows me where I drew the line as a carer. An emergency and of course I'd have stayed. But a few days in which he had the carers still coming in twice a day, and Terry as a backup if anything went wrong. And the emergency alarm. It was not as though he was completely helpless, I rationalised.

Such was the calm logic that allowed me to grab my own life back for a while. It did not, however, take account of the emotions of an old man who has lost his wife, lost his confidence and who is unused to being on his own. On my final Sunday in France before I fly home on the Monday, feeling stretched and relaxed, I'm strolling by the beautiful tidal lake in Hossegor on the Atlantic coast, sun blazing down and I call Terry – only to find there's been a drama in the night.

The mystery of the falling wardrobe

It was never possible to find out exactly what happened. What we know is that Dad had a fall in the night bruising the right side of his head which eventually turned into two seriously black eyes. We know he used his emergency call button and that people came, variously referred to as nurses and carers. We know that the time logged for this response was 1.30 am and that the log made no mention of a wardrobe. But we also know that Terry received a phone call at 5 am from carers saying a wardrobe was lying across Dad's bed and they couldn't lift it off to get him back to bed.

We know that Terry went round and struggled with the wardrobe eventually managing to lift it away from the bed. And that he went back at 10 am, after the regular carers' usual morning visit, and found Dad vague and confused. That he told Dad he'd be back at 2 pm to take him to see Mum in the home, but had no idea if Dad had taken this in. When he went back at 2 pm, however, Dad was ready waiting for him.

I was hugely relieved that in emergency Dad had used his panic button: his sense of survival had kicked in. He knew what to do. And luckily, that night, he hadn't bolted the door from the inside. Whether there were two incidents or just one, whether he'd been fighting with a wardrobe in a dream and somehow pulled it over, whether it was contact with the wardrobe that caused the injury to the side of his head, or whether that was a separate fall... The temptation was to try to get to the bottom of it. But Dad hated being asked questions. He'd close his eyes to indicate he'd had enough of being interrogated. So we never found out.

When he'd gone up with Terry to see Mum in her care home – this would have been about ten days or so after she'd moved in – Dad was hoping, apparently, for some sympathy for his night time drama and his two black eyes. For most of his adult life Mum had looked after him and now, more than ever, he needed her ministrations. Sadly, his attempts to get back to his accustomed position at the centre of her world were thwarted as her attention kept wandering. Most of her remarks were addressed to Terry.

Though relegated to the sidelines, Dad nevertheless was keen to stay on in the home until tea time: the reason, he managed to explain with some difficulty – he definitely had trouble finding his words – was that his microwave wasn't working so he couldn't heat up his meals at home. Terry took him home and fixed the fault, putting a Hungarian Goulash into the microwave, thereby raising Dad's spirits considerably. At that stage, Dad was still very interested in food. Eating was one of the few things that could cheer him up.

Panda eyes

By the time I got back from France the next afternoon Dad's bruising had spread to both eyes: he looked awful, like an elderly panda. My being back did seem to perk him up though. I guess he felt safer.

Worried about the bruising I rang the District Nurses but they couldn't come and see him for a couple of days. When I went round again later in the day I was shocked at the way the bleeding under the skin was spreading so took him straight round to the surgery. That day Dad seemed upbeat, joking with other patients in the waiting room, managing to climb the mountainous flight of stairs leading to the consulting room. Our Crossroads carer had been earlier, not Charmain but a replacement, and Dad had even remembered her name.

The GP showed no particular interest in Dad's panda eyes: all perfectly normal, he said. He didn't seem bothered by his fall and any possible repercussions either. We did however discuss Dad's medication and Dad himself volunteered that he wanted to come off anti-depressants. Might this be a good idea? Possibly, mused the doctor. 'We're guessing', he admitted but thought it was worth a try. Dad was on 30 mg a day of Citalopram. We could reduce this to 20 mg, then 10, then 10 every other day. And he also agreed to re-refer Dad to the Community Psychiatric Service for a new mental health assessment.

Assessing Dad's care needs

Now that Mum was settling down in the home, her welfare sat more lightly on my shoulders and I could allow concern for Dad's future to rise to the surface. The visit from the Care Manager for the Elderly was due on the Friday of this, my first week back, to assess what more permanent care package Dad needed. In preparation I tried to find out what he wanted for himself in this new life, separate from Mum though less than a mile away. He could, for instance, visit Mum every day if he wanted; he could eat some of his meals in the home if he wished or... But he didn't know. And I didn't know either. When I pressed him he closed his eyes and refused to talk about it.

On Friday morning the Care Manager duly arrives, friendly and quite talkative. With Dad you have to leave long, long pauses. And even then you often don't get an answer. Understandably, she didn't always wait long enough. After all, she must have had other visits to make. Dad wasn't saying with any clarity how he wanted to be cared for. Would he like to go to a Day Centre? He could perhaps attend, say, one or two days a week, for stimulation and company. No reaction.

He still looked awful. For all we knew, he could still have been suffering the after-effects of the weekend wardrobe drama. Rather than pressing him further, therefore, we decided that perhaps some 'respite care' in Mum's care home would help to get him on his feet again. I had checked and knew that the respite room was free for about ten days. The Care Manager and I reasoned that not only would this respite care mean he was looked after till he was fully recovered; at the same time it would give him first hand experience of being in a care home, so he'd have some point of comparison between being 'at home' with carers coming in and 'in a home' with the care on the spot. But most important, he'd be near Mum.

Not that at this point we seriously thought he too would go into residential care.

The Care Manager arranged it so he could go into the home on the Sunday (19th August) and stay 10 days or so till Thursday 30th – someone else had booked it for a week from 31st. While he stayed there she would work on her recommendation for a permanent care plan which she'd discuss further with me.

Fighting mirrors

We had, it turned out, another hurdle to get over before Dad reached that respite care room. On Saturday 18th, the day before he was booked in, the emergency carers, who were still coming twice a day, reported that Dad said he'd had a 'funny turn'. When I went round he was lying on his bed talking about fighting with mirrors, and how hard this was as they kept hitting him. Given he'd had a blow on the head a few days before I wondered if he was hallucinating. As it was the weekend I rang the out-of-hours doctor's service and they asked me to bring Dad up to see them.

The Emergency Health Centre is, as it so happens, just opposite Mum's care home. We sat in the waiting room for what seemed like hours but was probably only about 20 minutes. Dad always gets impatient at having to wait anywhere. Ironic really. I, who have lots of other things to do, am usually very patient in waiting rooms. He, who has no pressing engagements, can't bear to wait.

I could hear the voice of the lovely Irish doctor who'd come out to see Mum that fateful day she'd left home for the last time. Please let it be him that we see, I prayed, but in vain: instead we got a perfectly pleasant but not very warm and comforting German woman doctor.

Though I told her Dad had been diagnosed with vascular dementia, she did what I had come to recognise as all the 'doctorly' things they do. Theirs is a perfectly rational and logical approach that systematically checks all the physical systems of the body from eyes, through heart/lungs to mobility and much besides. What she didn't do is show much interest in the mental side even though her patient was an old man who was slow and known to have some dementia. I guess this approach typifies the Western approach to medicine: doggedly dualistic. Body totally separate from mind.

More urine sampling

At one point she sent us off to get a urine sample. I knew from the experience with Mum that doctors routinely check for urinary tract infections (UTIs) when working with elderly patients. Dad understood what was required so at least this wasn't like trying to get some pee out of Mum that Crisis Weekend. But the doctor's request, made so matter-of-factly, did raise the problem of doing intimate things for the 'other sex' parent. I'd wiped Mum's bottom on occasion, but never Dad's. He did those things for himself. Fervently I hoped he'd manage a urine sample by himself too. Standing outside the loo with the door ajar I encouraged him, and when this seemed to work, took the sample and poured it into the relevant container. The doctor tested it and declared him UTI free.

Because Dad had suffered a knock on the head, the doctor decided to play safe and get him X-rayed. So it was that I found myself spending another Saturday night up at Addenbrooke's Hospital in that same Medical Assessment Unit where we'd been with Mum so recently. Only this time there was no Alan and Sue to share the experience; just me and Dad. No fun and laughter. Just a long, long wait.

Waiting and waiting and waiting

They needed to do a CT scan but said they wouldn't be able to get to the machine till the early hours of the morning. One proposal was that we wait, have the scan, then go home. Not such a good idea, I thought, sending a 90 year old man with dementia out into the night. Did they have no imagination? The alternative was to find him a bed for the night, do the scan when the machine became available then I could pick him up next morning. I told them he was going into respite care next day which they seemed to think was A Good Thing.

The long wait tried even the patience I was so proud of. With vascular dementia attacking his word finding skills, compounded by low spirits, Dad doesn't have much conversation and the hours dragged by. Eventually, well after midnight, two orderlies wheeled him on to a ward – where we were met by an almost party atmosphere. The female night staff had a couple of visiting male nurses. With the two orderlies this made six staff laughing and joking with each other and with us as they got Dad off the wheeled bed and on to the ward bed. I left him in happy hands.

Holes in his brain

Omar, the kind young doctor who'd been in charge of Dad on the Assessment Unit, rang me next day to say the scan had revealed no damage from the fall, but did show that 'a number of parts of his brain had atrophied'. This was normal with very old people, he added. 'Dad's got holes in his brain', I remember thinking. This visual picture made more of an impact on me than the verbal descriptions of vascular dementia that I'd read. 'No wonder he can't function properly', I thought. The trouble with 'holes in the brain', I realised, is that they don't show; the person looks normal. That's why it's so easy to fall into the trap of blaming them for their lack of motivation, or their negativity. The trap of thinking, as I'd done with Dad more than once: 'If he could only make a bit of an effort', forgetting that his brain is like a colander so he can't.

When Terry and I picked Dad up next morning, he seemed quite alert and cheerful. We took him home, got some lunch ready and left him to eat it while we went home for ours. I'll be back at 2.30, I said, to take you to the care home so you can be looked after and get some rest. But when I got back he was in bed and didn't seem to want to go anywhere.

Respite for Dad

With hindsight I realise that we were still expecting far too much of him. Did I really think he'd have got himself ready for his stay in the home? What he actually needed (and wanted) was full time care. Even an hour on his own could cause him to withdraw into sleep, his way of escaping from fear and despair. So there he was dozing, no idea where we were going. And I had to get him ready for his ten day stay in Mum's care home.

I don't have children myself but on this occasion I had the distinct feeling of dealing with a child, feeling that exasperation of the responsible adult who knows we have to get going while the 'child' goes his own way, no sense of urgency at all. Dad had been in the same clothes for days, so I was going to need to get him changed before we went out. Note the expression 'get him changed', not get him to change his clothes. That was how I felt.

I produce some clean clothes and because I need to instil some urgency and help him dress, I have to see him half naked. I'm not sure I want to take this step of becoming familiar with my Dad's private parts. There's no room for angst, however, since the home are ringing to say 'where are you?' One of the managers has stayed on specially to wait for us: we really do need to get going.

To get out of the house quicker I decide to take the minimum of luggage, get Dad settled, then come back and fill a suitcase. After all, it's only a few minutes in the car. We arrive and he's welcomed by the manager; one of the carers shows us to his room which is separate from the other rooms and a bit smaller. It's nice enough though with its own bathroom.

After a short while I disappear to go and pack a suitcase: a mistake as it turns out as my disappearing upsets Dad hugely, and his distress worries the staff. I was slowly learning that I represented a fixed point in a confusing, moving world for my Dad. In that last 24 hours he'd been at home, then at the Emergency Health Centre, then in Addenbrooke's Hospital overnight having his brain scanned, then home again and now in a care home. That's a lot for anyone, let alone an old man with holes in his brain. I should have stayed longer before rushing off. That was the 'doer' in me kicking in. The suitcase could have waited.

'I can't live with these people'

I get back, reassuring him he hasn't been deserted, show him round (his room is in the 'ordinary residential' part of the home which has many more rooms than Mum's secure Unit downstairs), then get him settled in the dining room for tea. Like him, his table companions, both female, are of the slow, silent type. Next day, Monday, I go over to visit him after tea, about 6.30 in the evening. I find him lying on his bed saying he's been told he has to go to bed. 'I can't stay with these people', he says. His mood is petulant and he whips off his clothes in front of me and puts on his pyjamas. For me this is a very low point. I've tried to do what I think is best for him and it's clearly not working. He's unhappy and being childish. I'm unhappy and feeling guilty for bringing him here. I leave feeling desperate.

As the days go by he's still saying he 'can't live with these people'; he's also complaining he can't sleep at night (his room is over the rear car park which may have made it a bit noisy). Though he's looking better, this is clearly not the place for him. I conclude that in his case the accepted wisdom is right: he's better off in his own home. And so with the Care Manager we start to work out a care package for him to start at the end of the month. The main question to be resolved: how many carer visits a day will he need?

What he means by 'these people' I come to see are 'old people'. Dad was always a good-looking man with a certain charm; though shy he used his humour to win people over. None of us feels as old on the inside as we may look on the outside and I guess his image of himself was still of a younger man. So to find himself with people of his own age group (the average age in the home is at least mid to late 80s) was a shock.

Many of the residents were also in worse physical (though not necessarily mental) shape than him too. Where he used one stick to help him walk, many of them were bent over walking frames or wheeled walking aids, moving slowly. Very, very slowly sometimes. Here, perhaps for the first time, he was faced with clear evidence of ageing everywhere he looked. True he'd been complaining of 'being old' for a long time, but old age had never been brought home to him like this before.

Dad turns 90

Born in 1917, Dad was 90 years old on 23rd August 2007, a few days after going into Mum's care home for respite care. Alan and Sue were still away in their recently-acquired house in Cyprus, and Mum couldn't take in for more than a few minutes that Dad's birthday was upcoming, so it was up to me to organise his 90th birthday celebrations. A month or two back I'd nursed ambitions of taking him to the Imperial War Museum at Duxford so that he could revisit and perhaps relive some of his RAF experiences from World War II. On good days he'd said he might be up to it. But as the day approached he lost his nerve and said he thought it would be too much. I didn't push it as he'd been through a lot in the past few weeks. It wasn't as though he'd expressed a positive interest in the trip in the first place.

So instead I invented a two stage birthday: I'd take him out to lunch, just the two of us, then at around 4 pm we'd have a little birthday tea with Mum on her Unit at the care home. I'd asked one of the assistant managers for permission and they'd assured me this would be OK. On the morning of the 23rd I went to M&S and bought a deliciously squidgy-looking chocolate birthday cake and some candles. To drink I chose some exotic fruit juices as I'd noticed that Mum and Dad had no particular interest in alcohol.

Around mid-day I went over to pick Dad up, bearing my birthday gift, a rather fetching light plum coloured sweater, which he liked – it really did suit him and he kept it on for the day.

I'd agonised about where to take him for lunch: some places felt as though they'd be too noisy, others lacked parking. Eventually I'd decided to play safe and go to a local hotel which had plenty of parking, a lovely conservatory, and we'd been there before, the three of us, for Mum's birthday.

A better class of pensioner

For reasons I didn't foresee, this choice of venue proved less than perfect. When we arrived, the place was nearly empty and we sat comfortably at my favourite table. Then other lunchers began to arrive, in twos and threes. And as the tables filled I realised, to my dismay, that the clientele were, almost without exception, pretty ancient. They were lively, active, dynamic ancient, it's true, but ancient all the same. Inadvertently, for his birthday, I'd brought Dad out of the fire, into the frying pan. Instead of leaving the shock of old age behind in the care home, he was surrounded by a somewhat more mobile and sprightly version.

He only ate one course and didn't want any pud. 'A better class of pensioner,' he remarked, looking around. I wondered if I'd've been better choosing the gastro pub down the road, which would have been very noisy, much less comfortable and no guaranteed space in the car park. I can't be sure he would have enjoyed that either.

When we got back he said to everyone who asked that he'd had a nice time; and maybe he had. He went off for a nap, and I went home to collect my cake and candles.

'Happy birthday to you!'

Arriving on Mum's Unit a little before 4 pm, I decided the best strategy was to set up a table with the cake and put on the candles, then go upstairs and fetch Dad. Dorothy, one of the youngest looking and smiliest of Mum's fellow residents wanted to help me. Mum said she was too tired. The staff help out and I get plates from the kitchen, and forks too since I've chosen a delectable, but extremely sticky, cake.

I bring Dad down in his birthday sweater. Mum meets us in the corridor, and they embrace and sing 'Happy Birthday!' together in chorus. Ahhhh, murmur the staff. We sit down at the table, Mum and Dad and a couple of the other residents, where I've laid everything out. One of our 'guests' at the table is Gloria who's really enjoying the fun. Gloria has a raw energy and is in her element when something is going on. I light the nine candles (I thought he might not manage the full ninety!) and Dad blows them out reasonably smartly: we all sing 'Happy Birthday' and I start cutting the cake and handing out slices and glasses of juice. Gloria wants us to sing Happy Birthday again, which we do, followed by 'For he's a jolly good fellow'. We toast Dad in juice, then she wants us to toast 'the person who made the cake'.

Bobbing about in party organiser mode, I hand out sticky chocolate cake to all and sundry (luckily I bought a large cake) ...residents, staff, one of the seniors who happens to be around and sends word to another senior that there's cake to be had. Dad feels he's fading from the centre of attention: 'It's my birthday', he says to try and get back centre stage. They start playing the old time tunes CD and we all sing away, as Gloria keeps wanting us to cheer and drink to more people. Eventually I take Dad away, upstairs to his room, and another birthday cake to share with the upstairs residents after the evening meal. A good time was had by all – including me.

Decision time

As the days of his respite care went by, Dad gradually grasped the routine in the care home and seemed to settle in. He was due to leave on the Thursday, 30th August – Terry and I were going away with some friends to Norfolk on the Friday 31st, just for the weekend, so I wanted to get him settled back at home before I went. I would go over on the Friday morning before we left, and Alan (who was now back from Cyprus) would come over on the Friday afternoon to check all was OK.

I'd already discussed with Dad whether he would like to stay permanently in the care home or go back and live at home. He wasn't very forthcoming but from what I could understand, he wanted to go home, so that was what the Care Manager and I were organising. The same emergency care package as he'd had before would be available initially then a permanent package of carers coming in several times a day would start.

On the day he was due to leave the home, I could sense some reluctance to go. As it so happened, a room had just become free in the 'ordinary residential' part of the home where Dad had been staying, and had not yet been 'put on the market'. I showed it to Dad before we left. Though on the darker side of the building so he wouldn't get much sun, it was otherwise pleasant enough. Dad's chief concern was whether he'd be able to find his way from there to the dining room. That should have alerted me to the effects of his kind of dementia on his brain: that he could easily get lost. I didn't see it then, but I did do the walk with him, up the corridor, turn left and the dining room was about thirty metres ahead.

Such did not seem to be the behaviour of a man who 'couldn't live with these people' and wanted to go home. I asked the assistant manager, therefore, if they could hold the room for us till after the weekend, and she agreed. When we got back to Acrefield Drive I talked to Dad about his future. Though he was not easy to understand, he seemed to be saying he wanted to take the room. I thought he should have a bit of time to settle back home before making what was, after all, a momentous decision.

Scene 7: Friday 31st August: Decision day

Next morning I went round to see Dad before we took off for Norfolk: the door was on the latch. No sign of him downstairs. The carers had been – their report said he hadn't been expecting them, though I'd told him they were coming. I guess I thought he'd find the fact that they would be visiting reassuring: I think now it was because I was reassured by the fact that they would come.

Dad was upstairs asleep on his bed, the bed that had been 'theirs' until a few months ago when Mum had begun using one of the smaller bedrooms. This just seemed to happen, no announcement, discussion or fanfare. And as Mum got worse, Dad confessed to 'not really knowing when or where' she slept.

Dad is hard to wake, but I need him to wake up: I can't just go off and leave him, even though Alan is coming over later. We've arranged that Alan will come over on both days I'm away, Friday and Saturday. So I coax Dad awake and he talks, sleepily, about being hit hard; it's those fighting mirrors again. He seems to believe they are real: they threaten, he knows he's going to suffer, flinches as they hit him. I wonder, could they be nightmares? 'Your mother was there', he says, pointing into the centre of the room. 'I put my hand out to touch her and there was no-one'. We talk, quite relaxedly, about Jung, the unconscious, the meaning of dreams. He jokes – that's something he's still good at, joking.

I persuade him to get up. Once he's up and about he can seem almost OK. Yes, he says, he does want that room, the one that's free, in the care home. He doesn't give any reason, doesn't say 'to be near your mother', or 'I don't like being on my own'. Because he can't explain, I guess. His brain won't let him. 'Can you keep yourself safe till Monday?' I ask and he assures me he will. And so we leave for our weekend – and on the way I phone the home to say yes, it's very likely we will want the room.

Scene 8: Saturday 1st to Sunday 2nd September: Crisis Weekend 2

We have a happy weekend walking by the sea; no phone calls. None, that is, till Sunday morning, a message from Alan after breakfast as we prepare to leave. I phone him back and he tells me Dad has jumped the gun: he's already installed in the care home.

Apparently on Friday afternoon, Alan and Sue had gone round and found Dad so soundly asleep they couldn't wake him. He got angry, they said, when they tried to rouse him. Alan decided they couldn't leave him like that – so he stayed the night. At 5 am Dad rolled out of bed on to the floor. At 7 am Alan called the emergency doctor who came out but couldn't find anything physically wrong with Dad. Alan then rang the home and asked if he could bring him in. They called one of the managers at home and she gave her permission.

On Saturday afternoon therefore Alan had taken him to live in the room we'd looked at. Less than 48 hours after leaving he was back. Permanently this time. Being taken care of. That's what he wanted, I realised, to give up the struggle. Alan said Dad wouldn't make the decision himself, asked Alan to make it for him. Maybe he needed someone to give him 'permission'. But it was the right decision. No sooner was he there, feeling safe, than the fighting mirrors stopped their attacks.

Dad installed

What a blessing, I thought, that we were known, such that, in this emergency, we could get Dad into the right place, and quickly. And because we were self-funding (now for two of them, money flowing out in huge rivers each month!), again it was just a matter of writing a cheque for the first month; no consultation with the authorities, no hassle. So now Mum and Dad were both in a care home. In July they were muddling along at home, and in early

September, less than two months later, they weren't. Just like that.

We had car problems on our way back from Norfolk this momentous weekend. But we eventually made it – and I went to see Dad, who at that stage was not in great shape: the home had put piles of duvets by his bed in case he were to fall out of bed again, though he didn't.

On the Monday we'd had an appointment with the Community Psychiatric Service, the result of my request to Dad's GP. One of their nurses was due to visit Dad at home to re-assess his mental health. I called and asked her to come to the home instead: which she did though nothing really came of the visit and we never saw her again.

Alan had taken in a bedside table. I took in an extra chair and some more clothes. When Alan visited mid-week he reported Dad was settling in. I visited often at this stage; took Dad down to see Mum too. Not for long; he sits by her but she forgets he's there quite quickly. He's happy to go back to his room. I take him for a walk 'round the block', or rather through the various corridors, or to sit in the armchairs at the top of the stairs, greeting everyone who goes by. Otherwise he usually stays in his room, and sleeps. And sleeps. And sleeps.

The curtain falls

Thus the curtain fell on the most dramatic phase of Fred and Mary's dementia drama. Their lives, and mine too, had entered a new phase.

They were being cared for, together yet apart. Apart because Dad was still well enough mentally to live in the 'ordinary residential' part of the home, while Mum needed to be watched more closely on the special unit dedicated to residents with dementia. Apart too because neither had the mental capacity to ask to see the other – they were reliant on others, staff, me, Alan, to bring them together. But together too. In the same home. Under the same roof. Dad still mouthing a silent 'I love you' to his blond haired beauty, now grey.

Chapter 5
Together yet apart

Upstairs downstairs

Here we were, September 2007 was just beginning and Mum and Dad, their marital home abruptly left behind, were now in a care home, together yet apart. How did this reflect on my role as an 'amateur carer'? How was I doing? Not well, some might say. Putting elderly parents into a home is always second best. It's dumping them, some say. Shouldn't I have tried harder?

Yet what was the alternative when Mum's dementia turned out to be so severe she didn't even know she was going into a home, doesn't know that's where she lives? When Dad had promptly followed her in, thwarting our efforts to do the 'right thing' and keep him in his own home? September 2007 was therefore both an end and a beginning. An end to the muddling along, to the acting as if things weren't too bad, ignoring troubling signs such as Mum no longer remembering how to make a cup of tea. The beginning of knowing they were not OK, weren't going to be mentally OK ever again, of accepting their mental breakdown, going into the future eyes open.

In the most obvious ways my 'amateur carer' days were consequently over. I was no longer the prop on which their day-to-day lives relied. And that was a relief. What I found, however, was that my responsibilities shifted. From managing their physical well-being I moved into a more subtle and delicate area: helping them manage their relationship.

Though there were no double rooms in this particular home, couples who were reasonably fit mentally could have adjoining rooms, and one or two did. Our problem was that Mum wasn't in good enough mental shape to live next door to Dad in the 'ordinary residential' part of the home, so that wasn't an option. And Dad wasn't in bad enough mental shape to live in the Dementia Unit.

This didn't strike me as a problem immediately. I guess I was glad that at least one of them was still in touch with reality. What I didn't see was that Mum and Dad hadn't themselves chosen their living arrangements within the home. Mum had come in because Dad had said he wouldn't be able to cope with her when she came out of hospital. He himself had swiftly followed because he was falling and fighting mirrors and seemed to be afraid to be on his own. The actual arrangements as to who went where were made by the home in consultation with their relatives, me and my brother.

This was not remotely because we wanted to steamroller them – it was, after all, Dad himself who, after his respite experience, had 'chosen' to come into the home rather than stay in Acrefield Drive. We didn't have a four-way family discussion because experience had shown this wasn't possible. Mum couldn't follow because of her Alzheimer's-type dementia and Dad, because of his vascular dementia, was liable to put his head in his hands when faced with any kind of decision or choice.

Together yet apart, they were therefore in a situation of other, well–meaning people's choosing. Mum downstairs on the unit for residents with dementia who needed to be kept an eye on, residents who wandered, who couldn't remember where the toilet was however many times they went, residents with severe memory problems. Dad upstairs in the 'ordinary residential' part of the home, his dementia still allowing him at this stage to operate in the 'real world'. He knew where he was and could look after himself with help and prompting from staff.

On the plus side, all the signs were that Mum was happy where she was. In the early days, however, Dad was unhappy on her behalf. He felt his upstairs section was superior to hers. Where he was they had tablecloths, for example, whereas downstairs, where eating could sometimes be messy, place mats were often used instead. He could not see why she couldn't be upstairs with him. Though he'd lived with her descent into dementia, witnessed it more closely than anyone else, he still insisted she 'wasn't that bad'. With hindsight I realise he may have been questioning the arrangements that had been made for them. Whether it was because he was lonely and wanted her close, or he felt protective and wanted her to have the best, or a mixture, I don't know.

In reality, a good part of the problem lay in his own mental deterioration. If his own brain had been less damaged, he could have brought her up to his unit whenever they wanted. Every day. Several times a day. They could have eaten together regularly. The problem was: he would have had to keep an eye on her, be responsible for her, make sure she didn't wander too far off.

Getting together

And that soon proved too hard for him. Dementia sufferers don't generally sit quietly and Mum, as we'd seen in hospital, was a persistent wanderer. Hugely curious, whenever she came up to see him, they'd sit in the lounge together for a while ('like two lovebirds', Dad would say), but after a few minutes Mum would need the loo, or simply wander off, and before Dad knew it she'd be nosing around someone's room. He was too slow, both in speech – the vascular dementia, remember, had affected his word finding skills – and on his feet – he walked slowly with a stick whereas she was quite speedy in spite of her arthritic knees – to keep her with him. Of course the carers on duty helped. But the home wasn't so well staffed they could spare a carer dedicated solely to bringing Mum and Dad together.

The obvious answer was for him to go downstairs and spend regular time with her on her unit instead. He did go down, of course, though this usually needed staff, or me, or Alan to suggest it. Dad's planning and decision-making abilities were failing due to his vascular dementia so he would rarely initiate anything. Whenever I took him down I always felt he was soon anxious to get away. Perhaps he found the behaviour of some of the more seriously confused residents upsetting, or even frightening. 'Those old bats don't like me', he said, though he eventually got used to them and would joke with one or two. He seemed to feel a particular bond with a lady whose mental condition meant she would be constantly in a bad mood and repeating downbeat phrases: 'It's boring' and 'I'm fed up'. Did he empathise with her feelings?

It quickly became clear that Dad needed help to handle their 'together yet apart' existence paving the way for my new role as go-between. In those early days I'd visit about three times a week, and Alan would visit too when he wasn't away in Cyprus. Though I was no longer carrying them on my shoulders, I still felt responsible for their well-being. It was taking me time to adjust to the abrupt change in their living arrangements. And it was taking time to adjust to the starkness of learning that they really were losing their minds. It dawned on me only slowly that the home wasn't just housing them, but also had responsibility for keeping them safe, well, and as far as possible, happy. I still thought much of this was my job.

I'd often bring Mum upstairs to see Dad when I visited. And every single time she entered his room, she'd exclaim with surprise that he was there. For her it seemed as though she was visiting for the first time. Over and over again. She'd cross to the window, marvel at…at what? I never knew what so astonished her: 'Come and have a look at this!' she'd always say and I dutifully did. Perhaps it was the height, I thought, the difference between her ground floor life and this first floor vista. After the initial flurry of surprise I'd encourage her to give Dad some attention rather than the view, so she'd sit with him on the side of his bed for a while but his lack of conversation meant she'd soon get distracted. I did my best in my new go-between role to keep her with him, but often failed and she'd wander off with me following her along the corridor making sure she didn't get into too much mischief. After all, I was the one who'd taken her out of her unit and was therefore responsible for her.

Mum's wandering attention was a key factor affecting any time they spent together. The pattern when they came together was this: on seeing each other their faces would light up with pleasure. They'd sit side by side and Dad would want to give her a kiss but he had to get in quick or she'd soon be looking around for some distraction. Or sometimes she'd be embarrassed at kissing in public: as I'd noticed when she was in hospital, feelings such as embarrassment can remain intact where memory and comprehension fail.

The way I played my role was to try to orchestrate their meetings to help keep Dad's spirits up. I'd say to Mum, for instance: 'He wants to hold your hand'. And that would work for 30 seconds, then she'd be distracted again. Sometimes I'd hold his hand myself as he seemed to find that comforting. On occasion this would cause Mum puzzlement as she tried to keep it clear in her head who we all were. On one occasion we were, the three of us, in Dad's room, and I was holding his hand and I guess she must have forgotten I was his daughter and not a rival for his affection: 'Are you trying to get rid of me?' she asked. Concerned but not hostile.

Old time music was playing one afternoon and I was dancing with Mum on her unit while Dad was sitting down. Mum looked across at him and said to me: 'Are you married to him?' 'No, you are', I said. We both laughed but I was glad Dad didn't hear. Whether laughing meant Mum understood what I was saying wasn't clear either. As we'd first seen that Crisis Weekend in the hospital, laughter had become her way of responding when she had no idea what was going on. In an odd way, her choice of laughter as a tactic was a gift from the gods, seeming to lighten her loss of mind, turning tragedy into tragi-comedy.

Are you Fred? Did I have a mother?

On other days though she would be quite clear Dad was her husband. She still had, and kept for a long time, the category 'family' intact. She knew that Dad and I and Alan were 'hers', that she was not alone. She still had a solid base. But within that overall concept, who exactly we were on any one day could float. Sometimes when she and Dad came together she'd know he was family but wanted to check precisely who: 'Are you Fred?' she'd ask. With me, in the early days she'd announce to anyone who'd listen: 'I'm her mother'. 'I know, Mary, I know', the carers would reply with that infinite patience for which they deserve to be hugely rewarded. As time went by she'd sometimes get muddled pointing to me and saying: 'She's my mother'. Or once it was 'sister'. 'Daughter', I'd say. Did she realise she'd got it the wrong way round? Or had these names for family roles become interchangeable?

Though Mum knew our nuclear family, when it came to her wider family, much seemed to have been wiped out. One day, before she went into the home, she'd surprised me by asking: 'Did I have a mother?' 'Yes', I said in that matter-of-fact way I'd accepted Mum's odd remarks. 'Well where is she?' she demanded. Wanting to avoid saying she'd died, I talked about how nice she was, her mother, my grandmother. Mum didn't repeat her question. I guess when dementia strikes you spend a lot of time trying to piece things together and not quite succeeding. On one of Dad's visits to her unit, she surprised him by asking: 'Did you have a mother?' Another day it was: 'Did we have a father?' To her, with her Alzheimer's-type dementia, these were normal questions. To him though, with his very different vascular dementia, they didn't make a lot of sense. So I'd take on my role as go-between and answer for him: 'Yes, he did'. I hated to see him suffer and so found myself trying to protect him from the extent of Mum's confusion.

As for her siblings: 'Did you have any brothers and sisters, Mum?' 'No', she'd say though she had five, four sisters and one brother, with two sisters still alive. But then on the odd day she'd ask if I'd seen George, her brother; 'I'm worried about him', she'd say. 'He's fine', I'd say. 'Nothing to worry about'.

With that response I was aware I was entering into her world rather than trying to bring her into mine (the 'real world'??) by reminding her that George was long dead. I'm not sure when I learnt, or perhaps decided, to adopt this way: it was a mix of 'it feels right' coupled with reading about dementia and how it's more comfortable for the sufferer if we go along with their world than confuse them further by trying to correct their illusions.

Where are you when you're not here?

What we didn't ask ourselves was what Mum and Dad made of their 'together yet apart' existence as a couple. Not whether they wanted it but how it was for them to live it. What did they think was going on in their couple, in their relationship, in their day-to-day lives? How much did they understand?

To start with Dad seemed clear they were in different parts of the same home. He knew Mum was in the building even if he couldn't find his way to her unit – which required going down in the lift from first to ground floor. He never entered that lift on his own. He knew he had a room. He knew the way back and forward between there and the lounge/dining room, the route he'd asked me to walk with him when he first considered moving in to the home. It was the only route he memorised.

Mum, however, had no concept of 'care home'. She has never – or that's how it appears – known she is in a home, just as when she was in hospital, she didn't know she was in a hospital. She appears not to know she has a room. If you tell her she has one she acts surprised. She certainly doesn't know its number, though she can find her way there. But none of this seems to faze her. She simply accepts where she is. As in hospital, if people are kind to her, and they are, she's OK.

Because Mum didn't know where she was, she couldn't 'know' that Dad was in another part of the home. How could she when she didn't know she was in a home herself? Even though she often went to the upstairs lounge to join in with activities, and she'd often been to Dad's room, she still had no concept of how they both lived. Of course I'd told her many times that Dad was in another part of the building, but she never seemed to take it in. Or that's the way it looked to me, an outsider to her deteriorating brain, a brain that could no longer retain new information. By repeating myself I now realise I was falling into the 'if they don't understand say it again louder' trap. I guess I still believed, against the evidence, that at some point she would get it. She would finally realise they were both in the same care home. But she never did.

Making up stories

As a consequence, for Mum, when Dad wasn't with her, which was the majority of the time in spite of my and Alan's and the staff's efforts to bring them together as much as we could, she didn't know where he was. In the early days she'd talk about waking up and being puzzled, wondering what had happened to Fred. Not that she explained it as coherently as this – but this is what I understood. But as time went on, she'd make up stories – 'confabulate' – as to what had happened.

One day I heard her explaining to a carer 'I was married but we split up. He wasn't very well'. Ten minutes later I brought

Dad to see her, and she looked as pleased as ever to see him, the separation story forgotten. Other days, after they'd been in the home a while, she'd make dismissive remarks about him having gone off or being unreliable – again what she was saying wasn't easy to interpret but that seemed to be the gist.

Dad, for his part, sometimes interpreted her wandering attention as not caring. He wanted her attention for himself and he could see he wasn't getting it when they were together. So he formed the view she wasn't bothered about him, didn't care about him, didn't really love him any more. This fed his low spirits. Not only was he useless and helpless but the love of his life didn't care about him any more.

The overall problem was, I guess, that they couldn't talk together about their situation, about what had happened to them. They couldn't decide together how they wanted daily life to be because they couldn't have a sustained conversation. The closest they got were the odd times they'd have a little spat along the lines of: you don't miss me as much as I miss you.

In some ways, I now realise, they lived coherent enough lives as individuals in different parts of the home. Dad, for instance, had a running joke with one lady, aiming his stick at her as if it were a rifle; one of the ladies on his table would call him 'the man of the moment'. For her part, Mum laughed her way through her confusion and went on regular chocolate hunts in other residents' rooms. It was their life as a married couple that was unsatisfactory for Dad and puzzling for Mum.

The familiar becomes strange

Though I couldn't share the experience of Mum's or Dad's very different dementias, I could see the effects much more clearly than I had when they'd lived at home. Ever curious I wanted to know what it felt like for them and so I tried in those earlier days to talk to them about what was going on in their heads. Mum's mental shape was worse than Dad's, yet she was the one more willing to try and answer my questions. This may be because she still seemed – and still seems – to see herself as living an ordinary life. Her memory is gone, she knows that, but her curiosity, like mine, is intact.

As Mum put it in the earlier days when she could still explain herself coherently, she has problems understanding what we might be talking about because 'I don't have a picture'. She hears the words but the association, 'the mind picture', has gone. 'Let's see what you remember', I say. 'Do you remember you used to go to Tesco's?' I think she doesn't understand so I press her: 'What was Tesco?' 'A shop', she says. And who did you go with? 'Fred', she says as though the answer is obvious. Slowly we recreate the experience and she says she has a bit of a picture. She does seem to have some memory of this weekly shopping trip but we have to dig it out with great effort. This suggests, I guess, that the memory trace is there somewhere but the connections are breaking down so she can only get there with difficulty and even when she does 'remember' it's cloudy and vague. There's no 'Ahaa' moment when everything falls into place. She doesn't build on the memory or start talking about it as if she remembers clearly.

And yet she hasn't given up. She still sees herself as a player though not always sure of the game. I was visiting one day, about to leave and go upstairs to see Dad: 'I'll go and see Fred now', I say, 'see if he's OK'. And she looks worried and asks: 'Do I have to give him any money?' – when they were at home, she was the one who kept the household cash in her purse. 'No', I say, 'he's got plenty of money'. 'Did you give him some?' she asks, applying a reasonable logic. Again some strands of memory seem to function but she has lost the context. She experiences the present but has lost the kind of everyday understanding that would allow her to say where she is and what is happening.

Relearning to live every day

A key factor appears to be that the familiar, the everyday we take for granted, has become strange. From the outside it looks as though Mum, and her fellow residents, have to relearn to live every day. Their dementia gives them what's called 'anterograde amnesia', which is an inability to lay down new memory traces, so they are trapped in an eternal present. One of Mum's fellow resident friends, Dorothy, goes out of the room. A few minutes later she comes back; the seat she has just left is still empty. But she looks around, puzzled and confused: 'Where shall I sit?' Another day she wants to go to the toilet. 'Do you know where it is?' I say. 'No', she says though she's lived in the home for two years. 'I'll take you', I say and she takes my hand trustingly like a child.

For Mum, the big, dome-shaped lights in the ceiling of the lounge are a constant mystery. She doesn't know what they are, seems to be waiting for them to do something unexpected. Of course I tell her they are lights but she can't lay down the memory trace and so immediately forgets. I guess she's lost the picture that allowed her to understand the whole concept 'lights'. Though this looks like a big loss, maybe for the sufferer there are compensations. Visiting Mum more than three years after she'd come into the home, the big dome shaped lights suddenly came on and her face lit up with pleasure and delight. 'Just look at that!' she seemed to be saying though by that time she could barely get out more than a few words. What it seemed though was that the tiny events of every day take on a significance for dementia sufferers like Mum that the rest of us never even notice.

What I find particularly striking, nearly every time I go, is the way meal times have to be re-learnt every day. I'm rarely there at lunchtime which is the main meal of the day in the home, but I'm often visiting at the end of the afternoon. The evening meal time for the residents is 5.30 pm. In the half hour before tea staff lay the tables with cups and saucers and plates. The lounge is at one end and the dining area, with three tables for four, is at the other. Regularly I say to Mum: 'You'll be getting your tea soon'. She looks very pleased and surprised. 'Will I!' 'Yes, look it's nearly five o' clock'. I point at the clock. 'Where do we have to go?' 'Just up there – can you see those tables with the cups and saucers?' But she doesn't really seem to see – or rather she looks in the direction of the tables but doesn't have a 'picture' that can tell her what the tables and table settings mean.

When she's at the table, however, she more or less knows what to do – apparently routines, repetition, fixed patterns can help someone with anterograde amnesia manage some aspects of daily life – though she often gets distracted before she's eaten all her meal, forgetting I suppose what she's sitting there for. Staff tell me they often have to feed her as she can't concentrate on eating. Eventually sufferers can forget how to eat at all.

Time zones

The other effect of Mum's Alzheimer's-type dementia that's striking to observers is the mixing of time zones, the apparent ability to inhabit the past and the present at the same time. I first saw this in the hospital just before she came into the home. The domestic routines that had kept her functioning were no longer there starkly revealing the extent of her mind loss. At this time she'd be backwards and forwards between the present and her and Dad's courting days: 'Tell him Mary says don't marry someone else'. 'I will', I promise.

Some of the time she knows her age, or rather she knows she is very old. But asked how old Dad is one day she looked over at him, this 90 year old, and said; 'About 40'. At the time I took it as evidence of her being in a different time zone, but I now think she was simply hazarding a guess. She had no idea of the answer. One of the golden rules I learnt from a couple of the books I read on coping with dementia was: Don't ask questions. Note to myself: curious or not, I need to stop asking so many questions!

For Mum and a number of the Green Unit residents this mixing of time zones has to do with notions of 'home'. Her friend, Dorothy, often gets agitated, feeling she needs to get home to her mother. Like Mum she seems to have no idea she lives in the care home, even though her room is very close to the lounge with a large photo of her on the door. For me, home for Mum and Dad was the Cambridge house they'd lived in for 30 years, just round the corner from the care home, the house I was now responsible for and was renting out. But I had plenty of evidence that Mum had no memory of that house, nor of Cambridge either.

Occasionally she'd talk about going home, and I'd feel a stab of anxiety assuming, for a moment at least, that she wanted to go back to her Cambridge home, that she'd finally remembered it. Struck by a kind of 'magical thinking' (see Resources section for details of Joan Didion's book: 'A Year of Magical Thinking'), I still somehow believed she could snap out of this confused persona and be back to normal. What would she say when she found that strangers were living in her house?

But no. 'Where's home, Mum?' More questions! She looked uneasy as if to say what kind of a question is that: 'Haverton Hill', she'd hazard, or 'Billingham'. Born in Wallsend, she'd lived in Haverton Hill, on Teesside, in the 1920s as a child when her father, my grandfather, had gone to work as a wood machinist at the Furness shipyard. In the 1930s, they'd moved a few miles to a new house in Billingham. Or she might say 'Middlesbrough' where she'd worked up to and during World War II. Like Dorothy, home for her was definitely in a long ago time zone.

One of the other residents, Gloria, was robustly forthright about the predicament they all faced: 'We don't know where we live', she'd regularly announce loudly and surprisingly cheerfully.

For reasons Gloria articulated, people with dementia can appear helpless, and there's a temptation sometimes to make comparisons with children. And indeed 'second childhood' is one way of talking about old age. Mum asks my permission to do things now as I used, as a child, to ask hers. But the roles aren't really reversed. Not with the powerful history we share, for 90 per cent of which Mary was my mother. Helpless though she can now seem, she still is my mother. I just love her in a deeper, simpler way.

Care home Christmas

Mum and Dad went into the home in the summertime when the days were still warm and long. As the days shortened they settled in. Then, as if suddenly, Christmas was coming. Mum couldn't remember for more than moments at a time that it would soon be Christmas. When reminded she'd briefly worry about all the preparations she hadn't made. And then forget again. Dad insisted Christmas was 'too much trouble', but then, as the day got nearer, said he was looking forward to his Christmas pudding.

The home were very welcoming of friends and families and that first year we – me, Alan and Sue – had decided to accept their invitation to have Christmas lunch with Mum and Dad. As there'd be five of us, we could have a family table upstairs on Dad's unit. Together not apart. I arrive about 11.40 on Christmas morning; the staff have already brought Mum up into the main lounge: they've made a real effort with her clothes, nicely colour-coordinated in bluey greens.

I disappear to dump the large bag of presents I've brought in Dad's room – he's asleep – surprise! On the side table are his presents from the home: a bag of toiletries and a stocking, just as I and, I guess, he, had when we were children, with two satsumas, an apple, sweets and nuts. I wake him, wishing him Happy Christmas; he doesn't say much as I try to smooth his hair down. He has lovely hair, smooth and silver, no sign of baldness but the hairdresser who comes twice a week to the home insists on cutting it in a Mohican style. I see he's wearing the nice, plum coloured sweater I gave him for his birthday.

Someone told me he was dead

He's pleased to see Mum and wants to give her a kiss; she keeps turning to him then turning away at the crucial moment. Wanting, as ever, for Dad to be happy, I eventually manage to orchestrate a Christmas kiss, and Dad sits down. After a while Mum tells me a terrible thing had happened earlier. Someone had told her that he, Dad, was dead. She doesn't say this to him, not 'you were dead', but to me. She'd been upset, she says, so that when she saw him she was relieved. I think back: maybe there was relief in her face mixed with surprise and pleasure when she saw him. She repeats how relieved she is. 'You didn't mention it when I first arrived,' I say. 'I didn't know whether to mention it', she says. I assure her that if there's ever any really important news like that, I'll be the one to tell her. Fortunately Dad doesn't seem to be taking any of this in even though he's wearing his hearing aids.

We all drink sherry and then it's time to go to the table. One of Dad's usual table companions is a 100 year old lady who gets upset at having to move to a different table just for today. I feel a little bad about displacing her. I guess when you're 100 years old routines are important.

Alan and Sue arrive in a rush. I've already got Mum settled at the back of the table, Dad on her left, me next to Dad and opposite her. Dad holds her hand as long as she has the patience to leave her hand in his; he's still not saying much. We pull our crackers, don our paper hats. First course is prawn cocktail; Mum is very slow, going for the tomato, ignoring the prawns, possibly not recognising them. 'Eat the prawns', Alan says but she doesn't know what he means; there are lots of words now for which she doesn't 'have a picture' and therefore can't readily associate with things in the world.

The main course comes: turkey and all the trimmings. Dad is slow, not finishing his plate; I had memories of a couple of Christmases ago where we'd all gone out to a restaurant on

Christmas Day and he'd bolted down several bread rolls as soon as he sat down giving himself indigestion by the time the main course was served. We then spent half the meal trying to help him get rid of his wind! But not today. Eventually he does finish his meal, including the Christmas pudding he was looking forward to, but declines a second helping.

A parcel? What's that for?

After lunch we all went to Dad's room for the traditional family present opening, though Dad seemed ready for a sleep. Mum went straight over to the window as usual: 'Come and look at this'. I went over as usual but still couldn't fathom what I was supposed to see. Dad sat in his armchair. Alan started the proceedings by handing him his first present: slippers. No obvious reaction. Mum is puzzled by the parcels, doesn't know what they are, what they mean. But she liked the 'Christmas globe' that snowed when you shook it and played carols. Songs she does remember. Alan and Sue gave Dad a black and white cow that snored loudly when you pressed its foot. He managed a smile at that one. I got him to lie down on his bed where he seemed happier and eventually went off to sleep.

Alan and Sue gave Mum a parcel clearly containing chocolates: she said she'd open it later. I've noticed that's her strategy with parcels. She's puzzled about what they are and so puts them aside. I gave a her parcel containing biscuits. 'Do you want to open that one later as well?' Yes. When most of the presents are opened, I point to her two remaining. 'You've still got these two to open'. 'Have I', she says. 'I never knew that'. A phrase she uses every time I tell her something about her ordinary, everyday life: 'I never knew that'.

'God Save the King!'

We help her open the chocolates and the biscuits and she tucks in: thinking she might make herself sick I take a protective parent role reminding her she's just had her lunch. She's totally forgotten that already. We decide to go to the lounge and leave Dad to sleep: they're serving sherry and mince pies and it's nearly time for the Queen's Speech. I notice that when they play the National Anthem, Mum sings: 'God save our gracious King'!

We watch TV for a while: 'Finding Nemo' is playing, but Mum gets restless every few minutes and wants to shut the curtains. In common with several of the Green Unit residents, I've noticed she's uneasy when she sees darkness outside and wants to shut it out. Is she frightened, or does she no longer understand the difference between night and day? I slip away to see how Dad is: he's awake and says something to the effect that Christmas hasn't happened yet. Shall I take Mum back downstairs to her own room? Yes.

Back on her unit, one of the carers kindly prepares us tea and biscuits and we watch the end of the film. Mum seems tired. She talks about her memory, how she simply can't remember things. I chat to a couple of the carers, tell them how Dad said Christmas hadn't happened yet. One tells me he was giving Dad a bath and he, Dad, was happy and friendly, and had said: 'We're going to enjoy Christmas'. Yet on the day, I'm not so sure. The carer says he needs more company, someone to tell him to do things – as Mum used to do – to decide for him what clothes to put on. They are very kind.

It's time to leave. I go back to Dad and spend a few minutes with him. He seems better now it's quiet, just the two of us. He realises now that tomorrow is Boxing Day, not Christmas Day. He's thirsty so we go to the lounge where one of the carers makes him a mug of tea. He definitely seems more himself now that things are 'back to normal'. I go home to my own life, marvelling at its ordinariness, its normalness, its freedom from dementia. Did they enjoy the day? I wonder. Who knows? Probably not even them!

A 'funny turn'

Not long into the New Year I come home from a meal out on a Friday evening to find a message telling me Mum's had a 'funny turn' and is in hospital. They couldn't get hold of me straight away so they've called Alan. He and Sue have come down from Stamford and are with Mum at the hospital when I arrive at around 10 pm. Mum seems to have largely lost the power of speech, and she can't seem to open her eyes properly either, though she's wide awake. The doctors were fairly confident she had one of those urinary tract infections, liable to cause severe if temporary confusion in elderly people. They also wondered if she might have had a mini-stroke, hence the loss of speech. Or rather, she could grunt out words that we could guess at, but couldn't speak normally. Gradually, as the evening wore on, her speech improved and no damage showed up when they did a brain scan.

She certainly did have some kind of urine problem. Lying on the bed in Medical Admissions, she'd keep trying to get up to go to the loo. In fact she was wearing an incontinence pad but probably didn't know that. I was amazed at how strong she could be as she tried desperately to get herself up, gripping the sides of the bed, determined to go. The nurse is coming with a bedpan, we'd say. But she took no notice. 'Have they got a garden?' she said suddenly. 'I could pittle there'. A fine piece of logic, and almost the only clear words she spoke that night!

Mum was in hospital from Friday night to Monday evening: I took her back to the home in the car touched by the warm welcome she received from the staff: 'We've missed you, Mary'. As with her last hospital stay, during the whole three days, she didn't seem to 'know' she was in hospital. When I tried to convince her, she was almost indignant: 'Well, I never thought…nobody told me…'

'What do you think those beds are, and the doctors, and nurses?' Too many questions, I know, but again I couldn't help being intrigued, wanting to know where she thought she was if it wasn't in hospital. She gave no real answer but every so often she'd say something like: 'I'll be going now'. 'Going where?' 'Downstairs'. 'Where we live'. But she didn't go.

Though she was in some other universe, she continued to operate in this one, observing the other patients, uninhibitedly making personal remarks about this one's legs, which were indeed huge: 'Did you ever see legs like that, like tree trunks', or about that one 'she's a pain in the arse'. She would wander but in a funny way; she'd laugh and the nurses would laugh: 'Such a pleasure to have her. She's lovely', they said on the Monday evening when I took her away.

I hadn't been sure what to tell Dad, not wanting to worry him. But once I knew Mum was OK, on the Sunday, I told him she was in hospital but she was fine, they just needed to take a look at her. Once she was back and met up with Dad, he expected her to tell him about her stay. 'She didn't say anything', he told me. 'Did you ask her?' I say, still managing to imply it's somehow his fault he can't find the words he needs.

'She doesn't remember being in hospital', I explain, in my role of intermediary. Dad seems sceptical: I'm still not sure how far he believes her brain isn't working properly. In her right mind she'd have given Dad, and the rest of us, a blow-by-blow account of an event as momentous as a hospital stay. He seems hurt by her silence.

That was their predicament as a couple at that stage: he could remember more but couldn't easily string words together. She could chat in unfinished sentences and laugh but couldn't remember from one moment to the next. They lived this strange, shifting life but couldn't reflect on it, couldn't talk together about it, couldn't really help each other any more. Together yet apart. Apart yet still a couple, still together.

Chapter 6
Fred's downhill journey

As we all adjusted to our new lives during Mum and Dad's first year in the home, I didn't think of Dad as having 'real' dementia. With hindsight this is odd since he was the one whose dementia had actually been diagnosed by a doctor. I guess I was comparing his less dramatic, lower key vascular dementia with Mum whose Alzheimer's-style confusion was so obvious. Dementia for me had come to equal the confusion and memory loss Alzheimer's brings as connections between nerve cells in the brain degenerate and nerve cells die. Dad, in contrast, appeared to retain some grasp of his former life. Maybe I could only cope with one mental disintegration at a time.

Vascular dementia is caused by problems in the supply of blood to the brain, particularly affecting the cortex, the folded outer layer of the brain associated with learning and attention, memory and language. Symptoms can include problems with concentrating and communicating, motivation and planning as well as depression. Dad fitted this pattern, his salient characteristics much the same as they'd been for a long time: low spirits ('How are you, Dad?' 'Terrible'), not saying much and sleeping a lot. He'd turn up in the dining room for his meals then go straight back to his room, lie down on his bed and shut his eyes. The amount he slept worried the staff and they consulted his GP periodically, wondering if his sleepiness was something to do with his diabetes or maybe his anti-depressants, now at a much reduced dose. I think it was more likely his chosen way of escaping from a life that held little brightness, to get back under the covers and shut everything out.

Dad's dementia was there, of course, whether I fully recognised it or not. He'd been in the home just a few weeks when he seemed to be having trouble operating his TV. 'Why couldn't they have given me one with simple controls?' he complained. I show him the remote control, very similar to the one he'd used at home. 'You use this', I say, then realise he's looking at it blankly. I show him how to use it, and he practises. And seems to get it. That's OK then, I think. But is it? How come he's treating the remote like a strange, unknown device? For him as well as Mum the familiar is very slowly becoming strange, but because he acts more normally much of the time somehow I don't register his downhill journey.

There's another factor too: whereas visits to Mum could be fun, visiting Dad wasn't easy during those first months given that he was usually either sleepy, silent or complaining. Actually that's unfair: he still made the odd joke and managed an occasional smile but his dominant mood was gloom in contrast to her laughter. How did it happen, I find myself wondering, that my laid back, easy-going, jokey Dad has become 'the difficult one' whereas Mum, who'd been so much more 'difficult' for much of our relationship was such a pleasure to be with?

What's to blame?

How it happened, I guess, is that physical changes took place in his brain, parts became starved of blood and could no longer function properly. As a result both his mood and behaviour were affected: he could no longer do what he used to, or be the person he was. And yet I didn't think of it like that. Totally unfairly I am annoyed at Dad for becoming a 'miserable old git'. A side of me clings to the belief that if he wanted to, if he made a bit more effort, he could pull himself out of his dejection.

Rationally, of course, I 'know' he can't. Jane, the Community Psychiatric Nurse whose visits had led to his vascular dementia diagnosis, had carefully explained how his powers of planning and motivation had been damaged. 'It's not his fault', she said. Why did I not quite believe it? Thinking about it now, I wonder if it was because the effects of vascular dementia are largely about 'not doing': you don't speak much, you've lost your motivation so you don't do much, your ability to plan is impaired so you don't have any projects. To a sufferer this state of 'not doing' may be agony. But to an outsider it can look like a 'can't be bothered' kind of indifference.

'I don't forget'

I also underestimated how long Dad would need to settle in to his new life in the home. Oblivious to where she was, Mum had settled in immediately but this didn't mean he, with his greater awareness, would do the same. For a time his problems centred around laundry and not knowing where to put his dirty clothes. One day he said he'd like his underclothes 'hanging on hooks on the wall', reflecting the way that when he can't see something, it's as if it's not there – another effect of vascular dementia, part of the difficulty sufferers have in making choices and decisions. What he'd like is someone to pick out clothes for him and put them out each day. I talk to the staff and try to arrange more help for him. Their problem, I'm told, is that, though Dad says he'd like help, he is often up and dressed before they come into his room in the morning. He can still look after himself but his mental slowness and difficulty in finding his words means he finds the everyday a struggle. And if he doesn't know something he can't easily ask. He says he feels 'dopey' all the time – that's how vascular dementia feels to him.

I visit Dad one Sunday afternoon in late October. As ever he's asleep, mouth open. One of the carers comes in to ask him if he would be coming to the Church Service held in the lounge every Sunday at 4 pm. We look at him lying there and decide the answer is probably no. Alan had been on Friday and said Dad was fed up because he was constipated. I decide to wake him. 'How are you, Dad?' 'Terrible'. 'Terrible how?' 'I don't know'. He takes my hand, looking remarkably well with a good colour, definitely not on the point of expiring. He hates being told he looks well so I don't say anything.

He complains about staring at four walls all day yet resolutely refuses to join in any of the activities the home provides. Or that's the way it looks. It's only on second thoughts that I recognise that this 'resolute refusal' could be a consequence of his impaired brain. 'Is there anywhere you'd like to go?' I ask. 'Heaven', he says. My head understands, my heart is quietly breaking. I know he wants to leave the world but I can't help him to go. I get him up and we settle for a 'little walk', which means a walk through the corridors looking out of the windows. We sit down in the armchairs in the lobby looking out at the garden. I pull my chair up close so he can hear me as more often than not he doesn't have his hearing aids in. 'Do you want to see Mum?' He doesn't answer. 'When did you last see her?' He doesn't seem to know. 'She doesn't miss me', he ventures. In the role I've taken on as go-between I explain that she does miss him but her memory problems mean that sometimes she forgets. 'I don't forget', he says.

Another Sunday I arrive and find the residents gathering for the Service. Dad's there to my surprise sitting next to Mum though he's complaining – apparently he'd thought that he and Mum would just be sitting together on their own and feels hijacked by the Service. She's impatient with him. 'I'm trying to get him to…', she says. To what? Do something? Be enthusiastic? For a moment they sound normal, her getting on to him, trying to buck him up. Briefly I believe she's OK, their relationship 'back to normal' so that they don't need me any more. Deep down that's what I'd like: to be able to withdraw from trying to orchestrate their together time, to be able to hand them back their lives.

As the nights draw in, I notice Dad has trouble knowing what time of day it is, just like Mum had at home, but again I don't take his confusion about time as seriously as hers. One late afternoon he asked me if it was getting dark or getting light. Another day he was changing his clock, which was perfectly correct, because he couldn't believe it could be 4.30 pm and already dark. It is as if the annual rhythms he had lived with for 90 years are suddenly missing. The familiar seasons are becoming strange. As are the familiar routines. Around 5.15 pm I tell him it's nearly time to go along to the dining room for tea. He's disconcerted, says he doesn't know the way. As we leave his room, however, the route slots into place.

Vascular confusion

If doctors or care home managers are asked about the progress of vascular dementia, they tell you it's a stepwise deterioration. Where Alzheimer's is a smooth downward slope, with vascular dementia the usual progression is: ministroke or 'transient ischemic attack' (TIA) leading to a step down which then levels out so that the sufferer can remain at this new level for an unpredictable time, then another TIA and a further step down which then levels out, and so on. They don't give a timescale or spell out the final stages. To complicate matters further, vascular dementia sufferers can sometimes go on to develop Alzheimer's as well.

We didn't know which 'step' Dad was on when he came into the home, or how many TIAs he may have had since no-one had ever actually witnessed one. In the absence of anyone observing a TIA the consultant had noted his symptoms and behaviour and suggested 'vascular dementia caused by TIAs' as the most likely explanation. He was probably right but where the brain is concerned nothing is really certain.

What did happen in those early months was that from time to time Dad would have a day when he clearly was confused. Occasional periods of acute confusion is another of the common symptoms of vascular dementia. At first those days were rare: I'd come in and he'd try and tell me something that had apparently happened but then couldn't find the words. One day, for instance, he said one of the carers was trying to poison him; she'd given him water out of the hot tap. He seemed to retain that conviction he was being poisoned for a few days. Around the same time he'd told Alan a convoluted tale involving someone called Pat and a bucket. In those early days I used to try and reason with him, not accepting that his mental state could sometimes be as wild as Mum's. The key difference was that he came back to normal in between, whereas she never did.

Toothpaste and combs and socks

One January afternoon we have a chat about toothpaste. Dad says he hasn't got any. Or rather he says something I interpret that way. 'What's this?' I say producing from his bathroom a large tube of Tesco stripy toothpaste, the top all hardened, clearly not been used for a while. Dad peers at it, not saying, oh yes I have got some toothpaste, not saying the opposite either. With Dad I spend a lot of time guessing, probably incorrectly.

On this occasion, applying my own not his logic, I make a guess that he doesn't recognise the brand, that for him toothpaste is Colgate, since that's what he used at home. 'Shall I get you some Colgate?' I ask. Not much response so I ask again. This time he says yes. Maybe it's to humour me. Happier now I have a task I get him a tube of Colgate but when I take it in a few days later he peers at it with no obvious recognition, just as he had with the Tesco tube.

Around this time we also have regular chats about combs of which Dad possesses several, red ones, deep pink ones, blue ones, black ones. His favourites though are the red and pink ones; his hair is one of his best assets and he likes to have one of these red or pink combs in his pocket all the time. But they keep disappearing, usually because he leaves them in his trouser pocket when his trousers go down to the laundry. For Dad the laundry is 'that room' – a room he knows from experience that I visit and from which I then produce his lost combs. He doesn't know where it is but he knows I know.

And so I'll arrive and he'll try to tell me a story about his lost combs, and I'll try to figure out what he's saying: 'You mean…?' 'I find it difficult to tell you a story', he says one day. 'You keep interrupting'. He's right, of course. But if I didn't try and clarify what he's saying…would it matter? At that time I thought it did – I thought he was trying to express himself and I needed to help him because otherwise nobody would know what he thought or felt or wanted or needed. It was one of the unfortunate ways my love and care for him came out.

Another day the subject was socks. Though I'd labelled all his clothes I drew the line at sewing name tapes into lots of pairs of socks, and so his would get lost in the laundry: socks became communal items of clothing in the home I noticed. But as there were relatively few men living there, these communal socks weren't shared by too many different feet. Every so often I'd go down to the laundry and see if I could recognise any of Dad's socks and bring them up. On this occasion, however, I had a more serious topic to discuss so I moved on from socks to ask how he felt about whether we should be selling or renting out their house. I didn't want to steamroller him: what did he feel was the best? He didn't respond: 'Do you want me to make the decision about selling or renting?' I say eventually. He nods yes. 'You don't care, do you?' I say. 'I care more about getting some socks'.

The strikes

On one of my January visits there was something a bit different about Dad when I went in. When he has one of his 'confused days', there can be something warm and mellow about him. He's less sleepy, less silent and doesn't complain. The way I interpreted it, when he was lucid(ish), he couldn't see much point in life and tended to be low and depressed. But when he was confused he lived somewhere in his imagination, sometimes in a different time zone, believing he was at another stage of life, and at those times he was still a player, still had a role in life. During his first months in the home, his 'confused days' were infrequent, but as time rolled by they began to happen more often.

On this particular January day, he's on his bed, not in bed but lying on top of the bedclothes, in his 'hut' – that's what he said one day when I asked him what he did after meals: 'I go back to the hut'. At the time I just thought this was quaint, but then I did some research into his wartime RAF experience and discovered that airmen on air bases were often accommodated in Nissan huts. Home being 'the hut' therefore would make perfect sense to him.

He smiles and I sit by him, take his hand. He seems relaxed, looks round at the room, looks at the shape of things: 'Looked at from here that television looks like a van with three wheels', he observes. His gaze takes in the built in wardrobe, door ajar with the end of a duvet sticking out: 'The bottom of that cupboard looks like a duck'. And so we sit companionably; and then he mentions 'the strikes'. At first I think he's talking about the outside world, has he heard a news broadcast that I missed? But no, he's talking about the home. Says something about not having had anything to eat for 24 hours because of the strikes. Or to drink either. I think this is unlikely – but at this stage I'm not used to these confused episodes and so I'm wondering, has there been some problem in the home? But surely they would have made sure he had his meals. He doesn't seem hungry.

Then he mentions the darkness. Darkness? Yes, 24 hours of darkness. I'm still trying to find a rational explanation: he sleeps all the time, I'm thinking, did he go to sleep and not wake up till it was dark, then think it was dark all the time? The Polish people, they were the worst, he says. They were all on strike. There were a couple of Polish staff and I knew one of them had been on holiday. On holiday? On strike. Mmm. I'm casting about now.

Dad sticks to his story of strikes and darkness and nothing to eat. I bring Mum up to see him and he talks to her about the strikes, wanting her to back him up. But of course she has no idea what he's talking about. He seems bereft. I realise now what I didn't realise then: it was very important for him to be believed. Others casting doubt on what he said about strikes or darkness or Polish people were casting doubt on his sanity. And he was still aware enough for that to worry him.

Springtime

Dad's confusion could be elusive, taking me by surprise. On Mother's Day I visit the home with a modest present for Mum, feeling obliged to mark the day even though she has no idea what Mother's Day means any more. I've also brought in a few things for Dad – combs, hankies, Earol for the wax in his ears – and I've put them in a red cotton Christmas stocking I happen to have at home, just to make things a bit more jolly. They've both been together at the weekly Church Service and afterwards I take Mum along to Dad's room to open her presents. Dad seems in good spirits, though he keeps checking his watch and talks about having his tea downstairs, which seems a bit odd. By downstairs, does he mean Mum's unit?

'Shall I take Mum back down for tea?' 'Yes', he says. Will he come? He seems to be saying yes so we all leave the room and walk along the corridors to the lift but then he declines to come into the lift with us. I therefore leave him on the landing and take Mum down, back to her unit. When I get back upstairs Dad is sitting in one of the chairs outside the lift. He knows I have my coat and bag in his room and says I need to pick them up – definitely an odd remark. We go back to his room but as I put on my coat I notice he's taking his Christmas stocking with him, the one I'd brought in, wrapping the ribbon round his wrist. 'What are you taking that for, Dad?' He's going to the dining room for his tea, I'm thinking, but that's not, apparently, what he has in mind. 'Because we won't be coming back here', he says. 'We'll be going home'.

I'm thrown as I always am by mentions of 'home'. I have this recurring fear that their both going into the care home has all been a mistake and that one day they'll realise this and want to go back to the home they'd so abruptly left behind. I still have some kind of primitive belief that they'll suddenly come back to normal. Fuelled by this fantasy, I ask: 'Do you want to go back to Acrefield Drive?' But no, that isn't the home he's talking about and he's impatient that I don't understand. 'The one-room home', he says puzzling me even more. What can he mean by 'the one-room home?' If it's his care home room, then we're already there. Or does he mean…? I had no idea then – it's only now that I wonder if in his mind he was living in a distant time zone and the 'one-room home' was one of those RAF Nissan huts he'd lived in during the war. I persuade him to leave the stocking behind.

As we get to his table in the dining room, one of his companions is agitated, claiming the tea in her cup is 'from the person who sat here before' – she normally has a ritual of drying out her cup but the carer on duty has been too quick in pouring the tea. Dad too is agitated. He sits down but then it's as if he suddenly thinks: No, this is all wrong. He tries to get up, wants to leave. I encourage him to stay. One of the male carers he likes pours him some tea. He drinks a little and pushes it way: 'That's nothing', he says. Nor is he interested in the sandwiches. He wants to get up and go. 'But you haven't had your tea', I say rather desperately. I don't know what's going on in his head and he can't explain. 'He'll be alright', the carer smiles, used to odd behaviour, I guess. Not trying to get to the bottom of it, as I am because this is my Dad and I love him and want him to be OK. I can't bear to see him suffer. 'I'll look after him', the carer reassures me. I leave with a heavy heart.

Summertime

I've noticed that Dad perks up if he gets some physical exercise so I usually try and persuade him to come for 'a little walk'. Sometimes he shudders at the very idea, other times he'll come. If it's warm we might sit outside, and if it isn't we sit in the armchairs by the large windows that go all the way round the lounge/dining room and make it so light and bright. We look at the murals painted by students from a local college and comment on the brightly coloured ducks and boats and cows.

A wasp comes in through an open window and buzzes on the pane. Dad determinedly takes his stick which, fortunately, has a rubber end, accurately assesses the position of the wasp on the pane – and here's me thinking he can hardly see – and squashes it with his stick till it falls to the sill. Dead. He keeps on looking at it as though willing it to live again. But no, there's not a single twitch. 'Pauvre wasp', he says in a mournful voice.

One Sunday afternoon I go in and find the lift isn't working so I assume Mum and her fellow downstairs unit residents won't be at the Church Service, which is upstairs; and if Mum isn't there Dad isn't likely to be there either. The door to his room is open. He's lying in bed with the light on – I see his eyes open. He's not deeply asleep. He seems pleased to see me, and in fairly good spirits.

This time it's not socks but handkerchiefs he's concerned about. Several times he repeats that he 'had a dozen and a half' and they've all gone missing. Then he tells me a story about his watch, how it was taken away and a strap that is too long substituted but now it's back with the right strap. Mmm. He asks me what they are going to do about the phones…he seems to be talking about a phone box, no two phone boxes, one has now gone. Ever rational, I try to establish the location of the phones. 'Do you mean here in the home?' 'At home'. 'At home in Acrefield Drive?' When he sees he isn't making any sense to me he smiles and says: 'Let's change the subject'. Mum would never have the awareness to say that: I guess that's why I keep trying to make sense of what is probably not fathomable.

Losing touch

I tell him I've seen his next-door neighbours from Acrefield Drive. Surely you remember, they've got two little children. Not a flicker of recognition. You do remember Acrefield Drive? I have a real need for at least one of my parents to remember their former home. 'Where did you live before you came here?' He has no idea. 'What town are we in?' He can't say. 'I'll give you a clue'. And I start to spell out 'C…A…M…' but he doesn't pick it up. And no, he doesn't know the name of the building we're in either. 'You're always asking questions', he says, quite rightly, but not realising how much I want him to remain in the world I know, the world I'm dealing with for them. Not long ago he did know where he was, where they'd lived. Now he doesn't, therefore he must be getting worse. We go for a walk: 'I won't ask you any more questions', I say. 'That's OK', he says, 'I won't answer them'.

We go for a 'little walk', meet one of the Polish carers; Dad aims his stick as though it was a rifle – it's his way of engaging. 'I couldn't do without you, Chris', he says at one point, 'and the girls who take me around'. I think he means the carers. 'I can manage with that', he concludes. We sit down in the lounge and he sees that from the wing where we took the walk to his own wing through the lounge/dining room, open doors at either end, is a straight line. 'You go down there and turn left', he says. Actually it's right, the way to his room, but never mind.

It's tea time; he stands up but doesn't face towards the tables. 'I've had about six meals today', he says. No, he doesn't want his tea; he wants to go straight 'home' by which he seems to mean his room. I try and persuade him to go the other way, towards tea. 'Are you going?' he asks, suddenly anxious. 'I have to go home', I say. Suddenly it's as if his brain slots into gear and he remembers the routine. And it's OK. He's OK. He sits down at the tea table and I slip away.

Drifting into silence

By late July 2008, nearly a year after he moved into the home, Dad seems to be drifting into silence. When anyone asks me: how are your Mum and Dad? I say: 'Dad's stopped speaking'. He's not alone in this; there are others, I've noticed, who don't seem to say a word. Actually he does communicate, with nods, but in the hour I spent with him on 29th July he didn't say a single word. And on the visit before all he'd said was: 'It's hot'. I wonder if it can be to do with his hearing. 'Are your hearing aids working, Dad?' He leans back and closes his eyes as if to say 'Don't ask me questions. I can't cope with questions'. I take him into the garden – it's a warm summer day, flowers everywhere, but he just looks, as if he's tolerating the garden as he tolerates life because he has no option.

After that I become convinced that Dad has stopped speaking and only communicates in nods and some smiles. On my way in to visit a few days later I have a chat to one of the Seniors. 'Does he talk to other people?' I ask. At first she says no, then she remembers that a couple of weeks back Edith, who's on Dad's table for meals, was being even more outrageous than usual (something to do with her underclothes, I think) and the Senior had said to Dad: 'Don't worry, Fred. I'll change your table'. Dad had looked at her and said: 'What and miss all the excitement'. With this story still in my head I go up to see Dad to prepare him for an outing we are having next day to the optician's. And here is my silent Dad, suddenly almost a chatterbox. Though what he's saying doesn't make much sense, he's smiling and cheerful as he tries to explain how a baby was born in the room opposite: 'I didn't know what to do', he says. 'I don't know how overdue it was'.

I then talk to him about the visit to the optician – it's part of a national eye screening programme for people with diabetes; I'd wondered if it was worth taking him but felt I ought to. 'Do my consultants know?' he asks. I wonder if he means his carers. 'Yes', I say. He wants to know what the procedure will involve which shows me that one side of him is in the present, even if he believes a baby has been born in the home. One of the Polish carers comes along and he and I chat for a little, partly about his (grown up) son. Dad hears the word son and asks me if this is the baby.

The three sisters

Still cheerful and smiley Dad starts a story about three sisters who have made an appointment with him. I learn later that he went down earlier to Mum's unit for lunch; he doesn't tell me that though. Could that have cheered him up, or is it the events he imagines he's participating in? Leaving the three sisters he goes back to his watch, which is a perennial problem topic: the date section seems to confuse him. I've tried to get the right date but don't know how to work it. And what's more the names of the days are in French which bothers him. He wants me to remove the date section entirely so it won't torment him. When I say I can't he says 'I'm going to ignore that section then'. It's tea time and as we walk along the corridor he says: 'Whenever you come, you confuse me about time'. And you confuse me too, I think.

I guess what happens when you are confused is that you can't see the big picture any more, or only intermittently. In that way the effects of vascular dementia are like those of Alzheimer's. So Dad couldn't see his watch face as a whole, as an object with a purpose. Instead he homed in on a part of it, the date, which he saw as puzzling, threatening even, so that he wanted me to take it away. Something similar arose when the home decided to put up in each resident's room a photograph of their 'key worker', the carer appointed to take a special interest in them. The sudden appearance of the photo clearly rattled Dad – he's stopped trying to read so ignored the explanatory text under the picture. Next time I went in I noticed it was missing: 'Where's the photo?' I ask and he says something about getting rid of it. I unearthed it from under a chair seat and explained what it was for: 'Everyone's got one up in their room'. This news brought consternation that he's done something seriously wrong by getting rid of the photo. I prop it up on a shelf. We go down to see Mum: 'Good job we put that picture back', he says to her, as if to say 'We were nearly in trouble there'.

Autumntide

On Friday 17th October 2008 I visit in the late morning to bring Dad's hearing aid back after it's been repaired. He's sitting in the lounge wearing a rather smart khaki shirt I haven't seen before – someone has written FRED inside the collar so it must be his. He tells me later he 'got it free at the garage'. I learn the GP has been called to see Dad as he'd had a fall earlier though not a bad one. He was found on the floor outside his room. Before that, apparently, he'd used the toilet in the room opposite his own and was then found washing his hands in the toilet rather than the basin, whether that was in his own room, or the one opposite I wasn't able to get clear. I decide to wait with Dad for the doctor's visit.

He looks OK, except for some blood round his mouth, and seems quite cheerful, saying he's had two breakfasts. He also thinks my brother Alan is here though I keep telling him Alan's in Cyprus. He's sitting companionably with Jack, one of the other male residents. He refers to him as Mr Hill, which is definitely not his name. Jack doesn't seem to notice anything odd.

Dad goes on about toilets and plumbing – can I get hold of a plumber? He has two toilets, he insists. At this point I think he's confused, but when I check his bathroom there's a commode there from when they took a urine sample as well as a toilet, so he's actually right. I ask one of the carers to remove the commode to reduce the possibility of more confusion. He goes on about plumbing problems though I keep reassuring him they're being taken care of; then suddenly he says: 'I have to see your mother'.

I go down and fetch Mum up in the lift. She's looking nice, just had her hair done. People have been saying it looks nice, she tells me, but she can't actually remember going to the hairdressers. Dad's comforted by Mum's presence though she quickly gets distracted by an exercise bike she notices standing in one corner of the lounge and wants to discuss that. Dad tells me a story about a man whose wife went to Darlington and lost both her hearing aids which were then sent to him. He's quite articulate. It's as though his inability to find his words only applies when he's living in the present; when he's living in the past he gets his language ability back. He definitely has things to say even though they're not easy to fathom. They seem to make sense to him.

Where his 90+ year old self sleeps all the time, this past self doesn't seem at all sleepy. He even says: 'I need to take more exercise'. Amazing! The GP eventually comes, a nice, thorough young man I've never met before. Though I try to talk to him about Dad's mental state, he sticks doggedly to the physical, testing everything: eyes, ears, blood sugar…physically Dad appears to be in excellent shape. And he follows the doctor's instructions perfectly, not therefore demonstrating the confusion that's led to the fall and the doctor's visit. All the young man can suggest is that they monitor Dad's weight.

The doctor leaves and Dad seems uncertain where he is: he says he has several rooms, several homes. On his bedside table is a note he's tried to write at some point, then spilled tea on it. It reads something like: 'If you find this can you report to the police…I never…home…' Did he feel lost and was he trying to get home? As we go back to the lounge, I point out the room number on his door and his name. 'Oh that's been there for a long time', he says dismissively.

I try to get him to remember the number but he says I'm confusing him. He's very unsteady on his feet, as though his legs aren't working properly but we get to the lounge, and he sits quite happily, not sleepy at all. He looks good in his khaki shirt, the one he 'got free at the garage', asks what car 'they' drive – I don't know who they are. Talks about 'stuff' and things being settled. In his mind, at this moment, he's actively involved in some kind of life in the past, still a player. If that's so, it's a good thing, I think. 'It's sad', one of the carers says. But considering how depressed he is when he's living in the present, I'm not so sure.

Winter wandering

As autumn draws in and winter approaches, however, Dad begins to pose problems for the home. In the latter part of October he has falls and confusion, and most alarming, he's been wandering in the night. On his part of the home the number of night staff is small as the residents there are not reckoned as needing constant supervision. But Dad is starting to need more attention. The main worry is that he'll fall downstairs. Though he is a long way from the main stairs there is a discreet little door not far from his room with stairs leading down to Mum's unit though the door at the bottom is locked. Dad has been found on those stairs in the night, it turns out. I learn much of this in early November when the manager asks to see me.

What I didn't realise at the time is that they had already decided that Dad should go on to Mum's unit where they can be sure he's safe. They were simply waiting for a room to become vacant. I'm shocked at first as I hadn't imagined he was 'that bad'. I was worried too that he would be unhappy on the downstairs unit: he never seemed to like visiting Mum there. Why would he like living there? The manager drew a diagram of the stepwise deterioration associated with vascular dementia, and told me they thought Dad had suffered a mini-stroke the week before. No-one saw it but apparently he was 'like a rag doll' afterwards. What she was saying gently was that the mini-stroke meant he'd most likely gone down another step.

Something has to be done

If his dementia was getting worse, and the night staff were concerned about his wandering at night – something had to be done. Nothing would happen immediately, however, as they hadn't got a room free. The manager said they'd monitor him, and when I saw her a couple of days later she said he was much better. The very next day though I had a call to say he'd fallen again. They would arrange to get him a walking frame.

I visit on Friday. Dad's door is open and he's walking towards it. 'Where's your mother?' he demands, very agitated. 'She just walked out. I don't know where she's gone'. 'She's downstairs', I say. 'Do you want to go and see her?' 'What on earth is she doing downstairs?' He's agitated and clearly believes she's just walked out on him and disappeared. This is a new level of confusion in which he no longer understands that they are both in the care home but in different parts. I take him down to Mum's unit, walking very slowly – he definitely needs that walking frame.

Mum's sitting in the lounge with her friend, Dorothy, when we get there. I bring over a chair so Dad can sit with them. He immediately tries to have it out with her about her going off. She takes offence at his tone. 'Your hair's nice', Dorothy says to me, oblivious of the demented marital drama being played out in front of her. 'Do you do it yourself?' 'Yes', I say, as Mum says something incomprehensible about Alan. The mini-spat seems over and I try to help Dad get Mum's attention. 'Say something to her',

I encourage. He puts his face up close to hers and says 'Hello'. Mum laughs then turns to Dorothy and tells her Dad's just said 'Hello'. Dorothy looks at me: 'Your hair's nice', she says. 'Do you do it yourself?'

Still trying to help Dad get Mum's attention, I show her where he scraped his elbow when he fell. After a moment's concern she forgets. Dad is still convinced she's walked off but can't find a way of having it out with her. So he gets up to go. 'Do we leave her here?' he asks. Clearly he doesn't remember that this is where she has been living for more than a year. 'Yes', I say, 'but you can see her whenever you want'. I look over at the Senior for support. 'Yes, of course you can', she says. 'He can spend all day here if he wants'.

Dad's turned his back and is walking out. 'Say bye-bye', I remind him as you would a child. He bends slowly over Mum and kisses her; she accepts his kiss. At this level, she knows who he is.

Lovebirds reunited

The norovirus, or sickness bug, hits the home and relatives are asked not to visit, so I don't see Mum and Dad for a couple of weeks or so. But during that time, I'm told later, Dad had started wandering at night again. No-one lets me know what's happening – maybe they thought I'd try and object – so I catch the manager and discover that a room is free in the downstairs unit and they're transferring Dad there that very week.

I'm feeling shocked as I go up to see Dad for what will be the last time in his upstairs room. But he's not really with the world. A kind of blank. We hold hands: he likes it when I stroke his hands and arms. Then he comes to life, asks a couple of questions quite coherently about what's in my bag. But when I mention Mum he says: 'Is she working?' He too seems to be in a different time zone. Eventually he just wants to go back to sleep. 'I am finally an orphan!' I think to myself.

On the Friday they move Dad downstairs, I decide to keep out of the way. That evening I get a message from the home to say he 'seems to be settling in'. Two days later on the Sunday, I visit. As I walk along the corridor towards the lounge I can see Mum and Dad sitting together; Dad's wearing a green baseball cap. They look comfortable together. As I approach Dad looks up at me and says 'Frances' – Frances was his older brother's wife whom I've never heard him mention before; he hasn't seen her for at least 50 years. I remind him who I am and test him later: 'What's my name?' 'Christine Carling', he says.

Mum is possibly a bit more confused than usual; she thinks we should all be 'going home'. Or that she has to sort Dad out. He is positively chatty; he keeps proposing buying things, 'glasses, like in the paper, the 5 guinea ones', he says. He mentions ICI (his ex-employers) and the RAF (from which he was demobbed in 1945). He fiddles with his watch convinced it doesn't work: 'I'm going to trade this in', he says. He goes to the window and looks behind the curtain then sits down and puts his feet up on the table. 'Mad as a Hatter', I think, unpolitically correctly.

Mad enough to get himself back together with Mum. It took a while but he made it. They were together yet apart. And now they're together again. Though he's travelled a long way downhill over the past year or so, he seems happy enough. Today at least.

Chapter 7
What if they came back?

Mum walked out of their modest 1970s terraced house one Sunday night in summer and never looked back. Dad soon followed, missing her and disturbed at being alone. Neither planned nor prepared for their leaving. They simply walked out on their lives.

Meanwhile the house they'd lived in for 30 years continued to reflect their presence, Dad's shoes by the door, Mum's magazines piled high. Dad left with a big bunch of keys in his pocket. Mum left with nothing, not a handbag, nor a purse, just the clothes she was wearing and a few toiletries. When she moved in to the home we had added her clothes, a bedroom chest of drawers, some family photographs, a few knick-knacks and pictures for her wall and a brightly coloured blanket. For Dad we put on a repeat performance.

For the rest, the house lived on without them, the 1930s china cabinet housing a few modest treasures, the patterned carpets and wallpaper reflecting the fashion of an earlier age. Something of their old selves was still there though, and not wanting to disturb it for a while, I put a couple of lights on timers to try to fool the burglars and visited regularly. Like an extra relative, I'd go and see Mum and Dad in the home, and then call in at their old home to make sure it too was OK. Luckily it was summer and I didn't have to worry about the house getting cold and damp.

Looking back I realise I didn't know how to let go of the burden. For a couple of years or more I'd been carrying Mum and Dad and their home on my back like a giant snail. The load was lighter now but I couldn't see how to put it down.

Power of Attorney

In some very practical ways I couldn't have let go even if I'd wanted to. Though Mum and Dad had given up the struggle and retired behind the walls of a care home, their civic existence continued. They remained house owners, tax payers, pensioners. Someone had to keep their affairs in order.

Though they'd walked out on their lives without a backwards glance, they had not left me completely helpless. In the summer of 2006, after Dad's diagnosis of vascular dementia, I put it to them that they should each sign a Power of Attorney (POA) form so that Alan and I could manage their affairs when they no longer could. Dad and I didn't so much discuss this move as I proposed and he agreed. Understandably, I guess, he didn't like talking about his creeping mental decline.

At that time it was still possible to take out an Enduring Power of Attorney (EPA, now replaced by Lasting Power of Attorney, see Resources). The crucial factor about any Power of Attorney is that you have to sign the initial forms while you are still compos mentis – essentially what you are saying, while still of sound mind, is that if ever you are not of sound mind, or otherwise disabled, you authorise your attorneys to act on your behalf. For Mum, in particular, I was aware that time was running out. Though emotionally I didn't fully accept the severity of Mum's dementia till she went into the home, the practical side of me nevertheless saw it coming.

Power of Attorney is administered by the Court of Protection.

Thanking whatever deities were watching over us for the internet, I found the Court's website, printed off the necessary forms, filled them in naming myself and Alan as joint attorneys who could act separately. In August 2006 I invited Mum and Dad's neighbour in to witness the signing. Whether Mum had much idea what the document meant I can't be sure. She had developed a protective mechanism even then of nodding and saying yes even if she had no idea what was going on. With their neighbour present, her will to appear normal was strong enough to convince us all. And so they both signed.

This initial signing is simply an authorisation to take action, should it become necessary, at some point in the future. That point could be immediate or many years hence. If and when the signers become incapable of managing their own affairs (or just tired of managing – the signers themselves can ask their attorneys to have the Power of Attorney activated), the next step is to register the Power of Attorney with the Court of Protection. This entails more forms and payment of a fee. Once your POA is registered, the Attorneys become wholly responsible for your affairs.

When they signed the forms in 2006 I didn't register either POA, not straight away. Mum and Dad had been very independent people and I had a strong sense of wanting them to have the chance to manage as long as they could. Dad could still sign cheques, their bills were on Direct Debit and I could use Dad's debit card to order their groceries from Tesco Online and their meals from Wiltshire Farm Foods. Mum was no longer going out or spending money. Even the window cleaner, so I learnt later, had begun to ask Dad to write him a cheque as he saw Mum's ability to understand cash dwindle away.

By the time they went into the home a year after the signing, I had registered Mum's Power of Attorney, and therefore had the necessary authorisation to sort out their bank accounts and organise paying for their care. A few months later I registered Dad's. I've since learnt of families where the parents have refused even to contemplate signing Power of Attorney forms, somehow assuming they will always be able to handle their own affairs. Suddenly they have a stroke or a creeping dementia declares itself more forcefully. They can no longer act for themselves and the family have no authorisation to act for them. Getting Power of Attorney when the person is no longer of sound mind is both expensive and time-consuming. I bless Dad for his trust and foresight. And Mum for making it easy.

Clearing, clearing, clearing

Clearing out the family home is part of the ritual you have to go through when your parents die. Or when they are losing their minds. Only then, in place of the finality of death, is a kind of limbo. You sort and dispose of their 'stuff' while continuing to visit them, feeling they should be involved yet unable to persuade them to care.

Clearing out a whole house, two long lives, is always going to be a big job. Even a modest house like Mum and Dad's. There must be some people who dispose of their lives as they go along, throw away old bills, file only the absolute essentials. I am not such a person, and neither, it turned out, were my parents. Alan and I knew we'd have to sort out their paperwork, throw stuff away, put things in order. What we didn't know was how much of a squirrel Dad was, and Mum too. So much so that they appeared to have kept every single till receipt, bank statement and credit card bill since they moved into the house 30 years before.

That first autumn, in 2007, Alan and I would meet once a week, whenever we were free, to work our way through the bulging cupboards and drawers that had housed our parents' external lives. We were very slow, partly because we took a lot of breaks, sneaking off to the local Costa to chat, partly because the task was very tiring. For me at least. I'm not naturally a decisive person and clearing out your parents' home demands decision after decision.

What do you keep and what do you throw away of other people's past? When these people are your parents, if you're too ruthless, do you risk throwing out your own past too?

With hindsight, I think that for me the slowness was also a reluctance to let go, part of my need for time to adjust to Mum and Dad so abruptly leaving home. They had adjusted to us leaving home, I guess, all those years ago. But when we, their children, left, that was a natural progression. Their sudden leaving and apparently forgetting all they'd left behind had not been part of any life script I'd read.

Security and sentiment

We started the clear out upstairs in their bedroom. When they'd gone into the home, we'd emptied the contents of small chests of drawers, one on either side of their bed, into carrier bags to sort out later. These chests were almost the only pieces of furniture in their whole house that seemed suitable for their care home rooms. We thought hard about the rest, but their armchairs were worn and too bulky, their dining table and sideboard were superfluous; and as they weren't reading or doing crosswords any more there seemed no point in taking in the tall bookcase that had housed the reference books they no longer consulted.

Bed, bed linen and towels, bedside table, wardrobe, armchair and their own bathroom: these basics were all provided by the home. Their rooms personalised by photos, paintings and knick-knacks, has proved all they need, a lesson, I guess, in the ultimate non-importance of 'stuff'.

But that realisation came later: in the immediate we had to sort through all they'd accumulated. As we worked, two criteria developed: Security – anything with financial details should be torn into tiny pieces, or better still shredded – we didn't want their identities stolen; and Sentiment – anything we considered of sentimental value, we'd set aside and keep.

Not that these criteria were always easy to apply. Was it permissible to be casual about disposing of ancient M&S till receipts when they'd been paid by debit card and therefore held some financial information? Was it really necessary to shred credit card bills dating back to the 1980s? Though I am a cautious person, Alan turned out to be even more so, tearing into tiny pieces documents I would have disposed of whole.

Similarly, when we started, many things seemed to have sentimental value – they'd kept years' worth of Christmas cards, for instance, and we originally kept any that had a personal message, till that became too many and we started to be more ruthless. What was lovely was when we came upon a card from Dad to Mum and read his loving messages. On their Diamond Wedding Anniversary he'd written that in all that time their love had never faltered… 'The card says "Congratulations" and I think you deserve them all as you have been the solid foundation for both of us…Love you to bits'.

There were very few from her to him, though we did later find a Greetings Telegram she'd sent him on his 21st birthday, the 23rd August 1938, at his work address at the Teesside Power Station. Not in these drawers but in a mini-treasure chest – actually a pink plastic zipped container – they'd put together, possibly when they moved to Cambridge, containing documents and pictures from the 1930s to the 1960s that had sentimental value for them. This move in 1980 was the third major upheaval of their married life, the first in the 1940s being the emotional roller coaster of World War II and the second in the late 1950s when they left their native North East and all their family and friends to live in Bristol where Dad's employers, ICI, were opening a new plant.

Tracing a life

To a degree, I guess, our 'stuff' reflects the way we have led our lives. And in clearing out Mum and Dad's stuff we were laying bare the framework within which they had lived, at least in their latter years. Much of it was mundane: they'd shopped at Boots, Tesco, M&S. Mum had bought makeup, most obviously a Max Factor pressed powder called Crème Puff. She had drawers full of Crème Puffs, many only half used. And shelves of hair sprays too, standing to attention. Towards the end, it looks like she kept buying new Crème Puffs and hairsprays, forgetting how many she already had at home.

But some of it, behind the mundanity, shed light on their state of mind. Dad had been a meticulous checker – of bank statements, credit card bills, gas and electricity bills – and a careful noter – for example, of petrol purchased so he could work out his consumption, and of more general spending so he could keep track of where the money went. He kept life under control, it appeared, through attention to detail. And I remembered how distressed he'd become as this level of meticulousness became more difficult. As his feeling of day-to-day control broke down, his sense of life falling apart had slowly developed. And with it low spirits and anxiety though I'd only dimly understood this at the time.

Ordinary or extraordinary?

Looked at in one way we were uncovering the shape of the lives of two 'ordinary people', ordinary in the sense that they had lived quiet lives mostly in private, in modest houses, doing ordinary jobs. But is anyone ever really 'ordinary'? Even characterising Dad as a 'meticulous checker' was an over-simplification. When we children were small it was Mum, not Dad, who kept close control of the family finances, adding up every penny spent, stretching out their modest income from Dad's clerical job. It was only as they got better off that she handed over the reins. Perhaps it was the weight of responsibility that made him check so cautiously.

Alan confessed he'd been wondering if we'd find something exciting, something out of the ordinary, some secret that made our parents special. Instead we discovered a whole notebook labelled 'Hair Cut' and devoted to listing when they'd been to the hairdressers. Was this the height of boring? Or actually rather quirky? We also unearthed piles of photographs, many from the 30s, 40s, 50s, unordered, undated, unidentified, as though they'd bundled up their history into a big ball and shoved it to the back of a cupboard. The opposite of careful and meticulous.

To our 'sentimental' pile we added the presents Dad had received when he retired from ICI after 31 years of service. He'd ended up working in Supply which may have been where he developed his attention to detail. His colleagues valued his good-natured humour and had cared enough to write a poem chronicling his life. They'd presented it to him on his retirement day as a beautifully calligraphied scroll illustrated with cartoon drawings:

On an August morn, a child was born
A credit to his mum
'Mid zeppelins and nappy pins
His life had just begun.

As a lad – he wasn't bad
His schooldays were quite fun
But when he came to man's estate
World War II had just begun.

'PER ARDUA AD ASTRA' was the call
And Fred was full of zest
To fight the Germans was his goal
He did his level best.

In Air Force Blue, with Brylcreme too
To Canada he sailed
To gain a Navigator's Wing – he hoped
He got it – he never failed.

By Polaris and Dog Star and Bloody good luck
Fred made it home to dive and to duck
His parachute jump was the talk of the town
Good old Fred – always the clown.

Out of the skies and down to earth
Fred once more had to prove his worth
In Demob suit – shoes shining bright
He starts his new life with Mary, his wife.

To Wilton he goes with a gleam in his eye
In his design career, his limit's the sky
The years pass by so rapidly
But 'WILTON FOREVER' is not to be.

Imperial Chems have another site
And once again poor Fred is in flight
A Supply Man is his Destiny
And he takes up his duties and his lemon tea.

He buys in everything from Car to Cap
And even sells the bloody scrap
He signs the Orders and Invoices too
And then looks round for something to do.

As his days here draw to a close
What will become of him, Gawd only knows
With ICI he's made quite a name
And things are never to be the same.

SIC TRANSIT GLORIA CATERPILLARS!

There it was, laid out in verse, the first 62 years of his life from his country childhood in Cowpen Bewley in the Tees Valley to the

RAF as a navigator during World War II. He'd been to Canada and the US for RAF training, the only major overseas trip of his life, it turned out, as Mum refused to fly and they generally holidayed in the UK. In his RAF days he'd done a parachute jump marked by a caterpillar pin. After his first job at the North Tees Power Station he'd worked for ICI, first at Wilton, then Severnsides, near Bristol where apparently he was known for drinking lemon tea. A tiny surprise, the lemon tea. A small shift of identity from the Fred who came home in the evening to tea with milk.

The Hirondelle Club

Mum and Dad weren't ones for a social life, or that's how I used to think about it. They didn't have friends in the way I have friends I see regularly. I now realise this was probably because the social life they had grown up with in the North East was among family and neighbours. That's what a social life was for them. Though it wasn't Coronation Street, when they grew up and married and had children – and, up to a point, when I grew up too till we moved away to Bristol – family and neighbours were a ready-made community of people who shared a past. Work colleagues made another social group that, on the whole, remained in the workplace. What need was there for anyone else?

When they moved away from their roots, they lost the close family contact, and only slowly got to know their Bristolian neighbours. Mum went back to work where she had colleagues to talk to – that seemed to be enough of a social life for her. Dad clearly had a social life at work too – he was a member of the 'Hirondelle Club', which I guess involved having a drink, probably lunchtimes as I never remember him being late home from work. His fellow members, Roy, Lin and Angie also wrote him a retirement poem which they typed and got prettily framed.

For many years, the members of the Club kept in contact at Christmas until Dad stopped replying. When low spirits installed themselves in his heart, he would seem to resent anyone who tried to touch the happier man he'd been. News from Angie at Christmas became a burden, no longer a pleasure. Mum would nag him into replying. 'I shouldn't have to bother at my age' became his attitude. Even Angie eventually gave up on him.

What became of him

'What will become of him, Gawd only knows', Dad's ICI colleagues had mused. What actually became of him when he retired from ICI at their official retiring age of 62 was that, stripped of his routines, still young-looking and fit, not ready to retire, he lost his way for a while and became what we thought at the time as 'a bit odd'. He decided to get another job and my partner, Terry, and I proposed Mum and Dad move to Cambridge where Dad became a porter at Clare College where Terry was a Fellow. He worked there for around five years, thereby gaining a new routine and a new lease of life.

When Dad left Clare, aged 68, he was still fit but more ready to retire, and made for himself a domestic routine, Tesco on Tuesdays, bank on Thursdays, Mail on Sunday crossword on Sundays and the like. This routine took him into his 80s, by which time his body was starting to let him down. His leg got painful so he didn't like to walk and gradually his routine was eroded. As when he left ICI but much worse, his loss of routine made him disoriented and low spirited. He talked of feeling useless, as though he'd lost contact with any real, meaningful life. This at least was how it looked from the outside. On the inside, who knows what floods of unhappy feelings flowed.

It was never easy to know what Dad really felt. His school references, which we found in the pink plastic 'treasure chest', report a conscientious, helpful young man. His Senior English Master wrote in 1933 when he was sixteen: 'His success in the Examinations of the Northern Universities Joint Board last July is evidence of the general level of his educational attainments.

Work is neat and has shown thought. His manner has been courteous and gentlemanly and he has constantly shown a desire to be helpful. He has always been reliable and honourable and his character has been excellent. I feel sure he will perform conscientiously and to the best of his ability any duties which may be entrusted to him, and I have pleasure in recommending him.'

When on flying missions in the RAF during World War II, he said he didn't think about 'not coming back', even though Bomber Command crews had a huge attrition rate, nearly one out of two crew killed in action. His love for Mum showed in unstinting loyalty and devotion, and letting her be the boss. She was a stronger and more determined character than him, more volatile too. We children would perhaps have preferred him to oppose her more vigorously. But that was not his way. Did he support her so faithfully because she was his life? It was only in later years I realised how much he loved and depended on her. Or because he was too timid to fight back? Or both? Or neither? What do we really ever know about another person?

And as for Mum

As for Mum, though she'd worked, at least part-time, for much of her life, we found among their stuff less that linked her to the public world. When she left Stockton Grammar School for Girls – unbeknownst to her Dad was next door at Stockton Grammar School for Boys – having a head for figures she'd trained as a Comptometer Operator (a Comptometer was a pre-calculator, pre-computer 'adding and calculating machine' for businesses).

She'd attended the Middlesbrough branch of the Felt and Tarrant Comptometer School. Based in Chicago, 'Comptometer' was their trademark and they ran schools all over the world. Mum did well in her exams: 100% her certificate says along with the words: 'Remember that you have been trained to operate the finest adding and calculating machine in the world, and you are entitled to such service from us as will enable you, with your own efforts, to make the Comptometer of maximum service to your employer. Do not be satisfied with anything but the best results for the sake of your employer, yourself, and the community.'

Her training completed, Mum got a job with Dorman Long, a local firm which started in steel in the 19th century and later moved into bridge building, including the Sydney Harbour Bridge, and also the unusual and impressive Transporter Bridge over the Tees at Middlesbrough, which she crossed every day to go to work. Mum loved going to work and kept in touch with several of her Dorman's colleagues all her life. When she and Dad got married (on 23rd December 1939), if she'd followed the norm of the day she would have given up work. But not Mum. 'I'd always be running late', she used to tell us, 'and one day I was running to the bus stop when one of my old teachers saw me and called out: 'You can't expect to run a home and hold down a job'.'

She became Head Calculator before leaving to have us children, myself, Alan, and her first, a baby girl, sadly stillborn. This was in the middle of World War II when Dad was away in the RAF and she'd gone back to live with her mother: 'They just took the baby away, and nobody said anything,' she told me once. So she coped, carried on, kept her sadness inside.

Later she was called up as a Warden. We found her 'Call up' papers, as well as the certificate she received after the war thanking her for helping her country in its time of need.

Though she hadn't worked when we children were young, she confessed later that as she pushed her pram past banks and offices she'd think to herself: 'I wonder if they need anyone in there'. Mum wasn't a natural housewife in the way she seemed to be a natural office worker. But it wasn't till I was 13 and Alan was 11, and we'd moved to Bristol, that she finally went back to work. And always part-time. Though she loved going to work, she wasn't a career woman in the modern sense. A bit of money on the side, a social life, that's what she seemed to want from work. As was usual for her generation she saw the man as the main family breadwinner, and would get angry when women seemed to be asking too much and thereby, as she saw it, rocking the boat.

Though I'd get impatient with these ideas, I realise now she'd lived through a time when married women were expected to stay at home, and, in her small way, she'd rebelled by carrying on work. Perhaps her anger resulted from a fear that if women pushed their demands too far there'd be a backlash, sending us back into the home for good.

Significantly in Mum's growing dementia, it was work that stayed with her as she started to take an interest in job adverts, leaflets through the door or handed out in the street. She'd show them to us as though she expected...what? Maybe she wanted to apply: if she was living in a different time zone, then, to her, age would not have been such an obvious barrier. Clearly she was excited by these job possibilities and wanted us, and Dad especially, to be as excited as her.

As it was all the way through their joint mental decline Mum, in spite of her dementia being further advanced, carried on living, still intrigued and attracted by the world, in contrast to Dad whose chosen path was to trudge his way through the long process of dying. As role models in life I would have chosen my Dad over my Mum much of the time. But as role models for coping with ageing and mental decay, Dad fulfils all our worst fears about old age as a terrible time, whereas Mum has been a shining beacon of hope that even with dementia life can still be sunny and bright.

What if they come back

As the shoots of spring 2008 pushed their way through the soil, much of the house sorting was finally done. We could no longer put off the question: what to do with the house? Rent or sell were the two obvious options. Renting could produce some income to help pay their care home fees, but then so would interest on the profits from the sale if we sold – this was just before the credit crunch sent interest rates through the floor.

I acted as though we were seriously considering both options, inviting estate agents round, getting the house valued, discussing what work would need to be done before we could rent, and what rent we might expect.

The reality was more complex, for me at any rate. It was selling that represented a real decision – selling was final. Renting, on the other hand, seemed temporary. Not really committing. Somehow believing this was just a phase. I know it sounds nonsense but coping with loved ones losing their minds is a kind of bereavement, and in bereavement there is a surface normality but an underlying madness. In her powerful and moving book, 'The Year of Magical Thinking', Joan Didion illustrated this madness, what she called 'magical thinking', when she described how the real reason she couldn't get rid of her dead husband's clothes was 'in case he came back'.

I guess, somewhere within me, was some of that 'magical thinking': 'What if they came back?' If we rent, then it's only temporary, they can come back and things will be back to normal. On the surface, in my rational mind, of course I didn't believe they could come back. But in the swirling emotional maelstrom that lay beneath the surface I simply couldn't get rid of the house. Not yet. 'What if they came back?'

For me, that was why renting was the only real option at this stage. Not now, but then. It was ironic, therefore, that, as one of the estate agents explained to me, getting the house ready for renting would mean getting rid of the personal, what made the bricks and mortar reflect Mum and Dad, and not anyone else, and making it as neutral and impersonal as possible, ready for tenants to imprint their own personality. 'A lot of families don't understand that', she said.

She recommended letting unfurnished, replacing the bathroom, painting over the patterned wallpaper: a radical shift from personal to impersonal. If we were to go along that route, then clearly this entailed also getting rid of all their stuff. In my schizophrenic state,

I accepted all this. Renting was still only temporary, and yet gradually their imprint would be removed. I must have realised this was the beginning of the process of letting go.

Personal to impersonal

We chose a small estate agent, an energetic lady who offered to help us with the 'preparation for renting' process, getting quotes, organising the work, taking off much of the burden. Of course it cost much more than originally envisaged. And took longer. As did finding a tenant, partly because such patterned carpets that remained, as well as some of the patterned wallpaper we, and the agent, thought we might get away with, apparently put off a number of potential renters. More so since the competition for tenants was hotting up – with the credit crunch starting to bite, suddenly everyone wanted to rent out their house. The market was awash. We responded by getting every single wall painted magnolia. The house took on a lightness it had not known for a while.

When it came to getting rid of their stuff, we learnt what I guess many families have had to learn: that far from house clearers offering any money for the houseful of furniture they are taking away, on the contrary, we would have to pay them. As we'd already realised, Mum and Dad did not possess anything of value and these days, it would appear, there is no market for second-hand furniture unless it is original, special or antique.

We considered whether to give away the furniture to the Salvation Army or Emmaus, but realised they would only collect specific items, not clear a whole house. In an effort to save something from destruction, we made countless trips to Oxfam with all their books, some linen and knick-knacks, crockery and pictures. We took a few things for ourselves, sold a couple of the nicer pieces of furniture to one of the painters, gave away the china cabinet to an interior designer friend who appreciated its 1930s charm. And finally commissioned a house clearance company to remove the rest.

The last day

The day before the appointed clearance date we went to the house for a final go through to make sure nothing important was left behind. All the way through the clearing process we'd been finding small caches of cash in drawers, bowls, shoe boxes. When she was still going out, Mum would go to the bank and cash a cheque – she never used cash machines – for £160. She'd bring the money home, put it away somewhere for safe keeping then sometimes forget where. So she'd go and get some more. I'd used some of the hidden cash we unearthed to pay some of the workers we'd been using. Even on this last day we found another £170, some in a raffia basket we'd overlooked, the rest hidden in the depths of a linen chest.

The house clearers we chose were a long established family firm: I liked the fact that they had a history. The owner, who would be doing the job himself, told me a story about one clearance commissioned by the family of a woman who'd had some kind of brain injury and was confined to hospital, destined never to recover. 'She had wardrobes full of designer clothes,' he said, 'but the family wanted everything gone, so we took them away'. Only apparently, this woman did eventually recover…and was devastated at the loss of her clothes. 'What if they came back'?!

Leaving the house for the last time in its personal 'Mum and Dad' state was a goodbye that brought tears to my eyes though it didn't seem to make much impact on Alan. We were saying goodbye to their lives and all the stuff that marked their stay on the earth. And they didn't know, didn't want to know. But I knew. And I cared.

The tree

The house was emptied in late March. Our first tenants did not move in until early August. So for four months I continued to watch over the house and monitor its transformation from personal to impersonal. Actually it looked increasingly nicer, brighter and more spacious. The prospective tenants were found in early July but didn't want to move in straight away, and in the meantime made various demands, or perhaps I should say requests – they didn't know how personal it all felt to me.

One of these requests was to reduce the scale of a massive, overgrown pyracanthus bush in the tiny front garden, a tree that in autumn was always glorious with red berries. They said, with some justification, that it was blocking the light.

Pyracanthus branches are very prickly, and this one was intertwined with ivy to its hard-to-get-to core. Though I knew a gardener, a lovely young woman who'd been keeping their garden in order, for some reason I decided to tackle the massive, prickly beast myself. And so, for afternoons on end, I fought with the thorns, chopped off branches, pulled out ivy, totally engrossed though my arms were cut and scratched.

Gradually I tamed the beast, reduced its prickly bulk, freed it from its prison of ivy, lowered its tallest branches, shaped it into some kind of recognisable bush. I was very proud. My last act for 24 Acrefield Drive. As I nursed my scratches, my gardener came round to do a final tidying of my tree to finish off my efforts, my labour of love.

And as for the rest

And as for the rest, a young couple moved in to my parents' home and made it their own, carrying the baton passed on to them by an old couple in a nearby care home. They were living their own story which is not part of ours. Except that they turned out to be expecting twins. Two new lives entering the world to replace the old.

Chapter 8
Emotional ups and downs

'Dementia' entered my day-to-day vocabulary that day Dr Dening visited and diagnosed Dad. Since then I've read widely about dementia in general and Alzheimer's and vascular dementia in particular. What emerges clearly is that dementia is a disorder of the brain most obviously affecting mental processes. Memory loss, confusion, loss of awareness, no longer recognising loved ones....multiplying disorders of the mind. That's how dementia is generally portrayed.

Yet the brain is also the seat of feelings and emotions. The experts don't seem so sure where these fit in. They talk far less about emotions in dementia, and when they do it's often in terms of emotions as additional dementia symptoms such as anxiety or outbursts of aggression or withdrawal into depression. What often goes unremarked is that people with dementia continue to have an emotional life, just like the rest of us. There may well be differences – changes in feelings and the way they are expressed – to their pre-dementia days. Yet they respond emotionally to what happens to them day by day, hour by hour, just as we do. Some of these responses are indeed directly triggered by their dementia but many are not, or only tenuously. Or that's the way it looks to me.

When Grace, one of Mum and Dad's co-residents, says to me 'I feel scared' I guess this feeling may well be a response to her increasing mental confusion. Dementia sufferers often express fear and anxiety. But when Elsie barks out to Mum, sounding very annoyed: 'I can't see the screen', the feeling of annoyance reflected in her voice seems much more like a natural enough response to someone standing in front of the TV screen when you're trying to watch a programme. It's just the way she expresses it, loudly and by non-demented standards, rudely, that suggests a loss of inhibition probably brought on by dementia.

As for Mum, she continues to stand in front of the TV, appearing unaware of what is going on. Elsie barks out again: 'I can't see the screen', sounding impatient as well as annoyed. The carer on duty ushers Mum out of the way: 'Come and sit here, Mary'. And when Mum is safely seated, she adds: 'Then you won't get told off'. 'I hope not', says Mum with a glance at Elsie. I guessed – but cannot know for sure – that she might have felt the thrust of Elsie's annoyance, even though she wasn't clear why it was directed at her, or even that it was directed at her. But she would have felt it not because she has dementia but because she has always been, and still is, emotionally sensitive. Like Elsie's annoyance in the first place, Mum's sensitivity to it was a perfectly natural emotional response.

Whose emotions?

In my lay person's experience, emotion in dementia is both complex and subtle, the emotional responses of everyday life coupled with, and sometimes heightened by, emotional responses to the confusion of dementia.

Added to this is a further complicating factor. Since people with dementia can't always say what they feel, we – carers, family, friends, doctors – can find ourselves guessing. And sometimes we fall into the trap of projecting onto our loved ones what we imagine we would feel if our own minds were failing. Such feelings as we project are almost invariably negative, reflecting as they do our deep fear that one day we may 'end up like that'.

In May 2008 I watched 'Mother and Me', a documentary about dementia made by Sue Bourne: she'd filmed the monthly visits she and her daughter made to her mother, Ethel, an Alzheimer's sufferer who was living in a care home in Scotland. On one of these visits Ethel said she had nothing to complain about. Sue expostulates: 'You've got Alzheimer's, your husband is dead, you're in a care home!' That's an example of the kind of projection I'm talking about. 'If that were me', Sue seems to be expostulating, 'I'd certainly feel I had plenty to complain about!'

Once 'dementia' entered my vocabulary, I found myself talking about it quite a lot. And from these conversations I have become aware that the whole subject, and particularly the label Alzheimer's, evokes a huge amount of fear. When people say 'how awful', I have come to believe they are expressing, in part at least, how awful they imagine it would be if they lost their own minds. Not because they know how that would feel but precisely because they don't know. Much of our fear is fear of the unknown.

Mourning the person they were

Another emotional layer is often present too, this one to do with our relationship to the person with dementia. Some people experience the long, slow journey of a loved one – parent, husband, sister, friend – into dementia as a drawn-out bereavement. In a sense they go through a period of mourning before the person actually dies. Mourning for the person they were and can no longer be.

I empathise with these feelings and do experience them sometimes. Perhaps I would feel them more strongly if dementia had affected my parents more harshly. What worries me though is that to mourn the person they were risks reducing the person they still are to a non-person, a person who doesn't count because of the memory and brain power they've lost. Whereas in spite of the obvious losses, they continue to live, and to feel too even if they can't always express their feelings.

What do I feel?

Dementia, I have come to see, is a disorder of the brain swimming in a sea of emotion. The emotion is both ours, we who experience our loved ones' dementia from the outside, and theirs, they who experience dementia from the inside. We on the outside can, or think we can, see the whole picture, view the mental decline of our loved one, sometimes with anguish. But at the same time we are carrying on our relationship with them, caring, smiling, responding to their feelings while sometimes concealing and sometimes revealing our own.

What I know about my own feelings is that they lie beneath a calm, coping surface, reluctant to declare themselves too openly for fear of…what? Too much pain? Being overwhelmed by emotion? Odd really since everything I've done to care for my parents has been driven by my feelings. What's become clearer is that my feelings have grown and developed. And that topmost among them is love.

Love

One of the remarks that stayed with me from Sue Bourne's 'Mother and Me' was about love. 'I've fallen in love with my mother', she said, or at least that's what I remember her saying. She and Ethel, it appears, hadn't always had an easy relationship. But now, with Ethel suffering from dementia, everything seemed so much simpler. She could love her mother without reservation, without any of the old battles coming between.

I remembered it, I guess, because it chimes with my own feelings. Mum and I didn't always have an easy relationship either. I was a perverse teenager, and we had a real gift for misunderstanding each other. As adults we saw the world through very different eyes, though as we grew older our differences seemed to matter less. Then, as Mum's dementia began to take hold, and I slipped slowly into the role of 'responsible adult', so her anxieties seemed to slip away releasing her freer, more mischievous and fun side.

The response that has since welled up in me has been of a simple love, simply expressed by holding her hand, singing together, taking her for a walk and delighting in her rediscovery of the world each time we take a familiar path. In this one and only way her dementia has been a gift.

Sadness

Second most is sadness, for Dad this time. I was always a bit of a Daddy's girl and loved my Dad in a simple way. As his legs began to give him pain, and low spirits set in – this was during the years before his vascular dementia was diagnosed – the way he felt his life to be a burden sat on my shoulders too.

I saw a counsellor at one point, and in one of our sessions I talked about my Dad's anguish. We did an exercise together, a visualisation that made a big impression. Think about your Dad, she said, picture him and you. Where on your body do you feel a connection? I pointed to my chest that seemed linked to his chest, and my eyes that seemed joined somehow to his.

Think about that connection, she continued. What's it made from? To my surprise, in response, an image of a huge, heavy, rusty piece of railway line popped into my head. Just like that. Very vivid. What did I need to cut through it? she asked. I don't know – some kind of heavy metal cutting equipment. Who did I need to help me? The visualisation continued: with help I got hold of the metal cutting equipment and sawed through the big, heavy rail watching it fall away, separating me from my Dad. And then we did the same with the other connection through the eyes: a much slimmer metal bar. What a great sense of relief! I hadn't been aware of just how much I'd been taking Dad's pain and depression into my own body, my own self. I saw Dad almost immediately after that counselling session and my new-found lightness seemed to brighten him up too.

I know from that experience that I was inclined to take on my Dad's suffering, feeling sad at his sadness, especially when I looked into his eyes that could seem to be pleading for release. Yet I couldn't release him until his body was ready. And so I often felt sad. And helpless too because nothing I could do would be enough to lift his deep-seated despair.

I feel sadness too as I walk about the town and recall their routines: today I passed the spot where Dad used to wait in the car to pick up Mum when she'd finished looking round the shops. An ordinary sadness for an ordinary way of life that's ended. Maybe after all I am mourning the people they can no longer be.

Love and sadness loom large, but I also move around among a host of other feelings including, in no special order:

Relief

That they are well looked after and treated with kindness so that I don't have to shoulder as much of the burden as I did before. Though I'm still the 'responsible adult' in the family, the home have day-to-day responsibility for their well-being and welfare. I'm relieved to have a lot of my own life back.

Anxiety and fear

Ever present is that feeling that the phone could ring at any time, something could happen and suddenly from pottering along, they're dying. Or one of them. And how would the other one cope? More insidious than anxiety around their dying is the fear that, as their dementia worsens, they will suffer more. Mum losing her sunniness. Dad sinking even further into himself. Fear of not knowing. Fear of the unknown.

Joy

At the simple times we have had together, sing-alongs with Mum and Dorothy, all the old songs, full of feelings. Love, longing, hope. 'We'll meet again, don't know where, don't know when'... 'I'll be with you in apple blossom time'... 'There'll be bluebirds over the white cliffs of Dover'.... Dad stroking my hand, still managing the occasional joke, pretending to be scared when I 'attack' him with my favourite soft toy dog: big eyes and a woolly hat. A dispassionate onlooker might think it's sad, even pathetic, that it's come to this: playing together with soft toys. But it's a way of communicating, and when Dad responds, I feel a flash of joy.

Weariness

Sometimes at this focus on old age and decay when, for my own health and strength, I need to dwell more in the realms of the young and fit.

Amazement

At the complexity of the human brain – and the strength of the human spirit.

What do they feel?

We can't know, not for sure. And though in some ways people with dementia feel just like the rest of us, in other ways, of course, they do not. If you are confused a lot of the time and you can't remember what's just happened, some kind of emotional reaction will arise. Anxious or agitated feelings are going to be common.

But such feelings are not inevitable, and, for any one individual, they're never the whole picture but rather part of a rich mix of everyday emotions that make them who they are, who they continue to be.

Though we can't know, we can guess. Rightly or wrongly. And we can observe scenes that play out. Scenes like these, the ones that follow, scenes of joy, scenes of sadness.

Scenes of joy and sadness

Scene 1: 'You're very pretty'

This conversation took place when Dad was less silent than he later became. I, you'll notice, am playing my go-between role.

Mary has been to the home's hairdresser. Her hair looks particularly nice.

Fred: You're very pretty.

Mary doesn't seem to take this in.

Chris: He says you're very pretty.

Mary looks coy.

Fred: She was very pretty when I met her. And she's very pretty now.

Fred and Mary hold hands.

Where Mum soon lost her sense of time, Dad kept much more of a sense of continuity. He remained aware that his love for Mary had been a constant in his life and that he felt the same about her in his nineties as he'd felt at seventeen when they met.

Scene 2: Fun and games shopping for clothes

Mum came into the home with lots of clothes but her love of chocolates, pinching any chocolates she could find, had taken its toll. She'd put on weight. She who in sound mind had scorned 'fatties', was bursting out of her blouses and skirts. Time then to do some shopping, and no need to go into town. A travelling clothes shop came to the home one Friday morning and set up in the downstairs lounge.

Mary smiles at all and sundry; staff greet her as they pass through. She has no real idea what is going on so Chris picks out a checked skirt she thinks might do. She takes Mary's hand and leads her into the loo to try the skirt on. Mary has other ideas.

Chris: Let's take your skirt off so we can try this on.

Mary: (spotting the loo) I need a pittle.

Chris has an 'oh no' moment, recovers and helps with the pittle. With difficulty she gets Mary into the new skirt. It's a bit long but the waist fits. They go out into the corridor and bump into one of the Seniors.

Senior: Hello, Mary.

Mary beams in reply.

Chris: She's been trying on a new skirt. What do you think?

Senior: (checking fit) It's very nice. What do you think, Mary?

But Mary's attention has been diverted by one of the young male carers she's fond of. She's waving to him and smiling. He stops to chat. Chris picks out two more skirts and the Senior helps Mary try them on. Passing carers chip in their views. Then it's time for blouses. Mary tries one on and sits in a chair. Two young carers come by and admire the new blouse. Mary laughs with them and they stay longer and inspect her new clothes.

Chris: (to the seller) We'll have these three skirts and these three blouses. (To Mary) Do you want to keep them on? The ones you've got on? (to the Senior who is coming back through) Oh yes, she'll need name tapes sewn in, won't she?

The Senior talks to the lady who works in the laundry who says she'll do them straight away. Chris takes Mary into the laundry. She's fascinated by all the notices pinned up and reads them aloud. The laundry lady is kind and patient, shows her where the clothes baskets are with every resident's name on. Mary's still reading out the notices as she and Chris leave. She laughs with the two young carers who are still there. Chris overhears one of them say they've never known anyone laugh so much. Mary peers into the office and waves at the young male carer who's now sitting at a desk. Chris takes Mary back to her unit. As they walk down the corridor with one of the carers on duty:

Chris: Do you like your new skirt?

Mary: Yes…but it's a bit long.

Chris: It'll keep you warm in winter.

Dorothy: (seeing Mary in her new skirt; she's also wearing a check skirt) It's like mine.

Mary and Dorothy compare skirts. Chris slips away.

Clothes shopping with Mum is fun, I remember thinking. She creates lightness around her and that's a gift. She can be a gift to others even though her dementia is becoming increasingly severe.

Scene 3: 'Sick to death'

When Dad went down to live on Mum's unit, everyone agreed he was 'better'; he certainly seemed happier to have Mum back in his daily life. At the same time, particularly during the early months, he was more aware than Mum that he was living with people who behaved oddly.

Chris and Fred are sitting together in the lounge on one of his clearer and more aware days.

Chris: Do you remember what this place is called, here where you're living?

Fred: Dizzy House!

He looks around at the other residents, some of them restless and wandering.

Chris: Are you alright, Dad?

Fred: I'm sick to death of being here.

Chris: It'll be tea time soon.

Fred: I'm sick to death of drinking tea.

With Dad there was always the feeling that he was aware of time stretching ahead, empty, and that there was nothing he could do but sit (or more often lie in bed) and wait.

Scene 4: 'For it is Mary, Mary...'

Alan and his wife, Sue, are talented singers and they'd volunteered to put on a concert at Mum and Dad's care home. They arrive, Sue in evening dress, Alan in a dinner jacket together with three equally smart friends. The Carling Singers, they call themselves, for this afternoon at least.

Alan has put the programme together: a selection of old time songs and hits from well-known musicals. He's given out song sheets so the audience can sing along.

The residents are sitting in a circle together with some of the staff including the manager and assistant managers. Mary and Fred are there, sitting side by side, and Chris has come too – she is sitting on Fred's right, singing along into his ear, which encourages him to join in too. The concert is well under way – and it's Alan's turn for a solo. But instead of standing by the piano, he comes right into the circle, and stands in front of his mother, Mary.

Alan: (singing to his Mum):

For it is Mary, Mary,
Plain as any name can be.
But with propriety, society
Will say Marie.

But it was Mary, Mary,
Long before the fashions came,
And there is something there
That sounds so square,
It's a grand old name.

*This is the refrain of this old song: he sings the two
verses too, and ends on the refrain.*

*Chris feels tears rolling down her face. The manager
and assistants are choked up too. Alan kisses Mary
to enthusiastic applause.*

Mary herself is happy to be the centre of attention
but she's not quite sure why. She's happy to be
with her son, but not really clear that he's singing
to her. It's us, the others, those of us who still
have our marbles, that are moved to tears by the
poignancy of it all: a 60+ year old son serenading
his 90+ year old frail-minded mother, showing his
love for all to see.

Scene 5: 'She's much better now'

I'd been worried that Mum was losing her language;
she was getting hard to understand and never
finished a sentence. Then one day I visited and felt
I'd been worrying unnecessarily: her speech seemed
much better. One of the regular carers was there,
standing behind Mum's chair. In order to talk to her,

I stood up while Mum was still sitting down. It meant we were talking over her head.

Chris and the carer chat about Mary and Chris's worry about Mary's deteriorating language which the carer hasn't really noticed.

Chris: (patting Mary's head) Anyway, she's much better now.

Carer: Yes, she's fine. Aren't you, Mary?

Mary doesn't answer. Instead she reaches up towards Chris indicating she wants Chris to bend her head down. Puzzled at first Chris bends her head.

Mary: (patting Chris's head) She's much better now.

Chris realises that Mary is retaliating, showing what it's like to be patted on the head and talked over.

Chris: Sorry. I didn't mean to talk over your head. It was just that Kate was standing up…

I remember thinking this was an example of a 'normal emotional reaction' on Mum's part rather than an emotion triggered by her dementia. A sensitive soul, she hated it if she ever imagined (and she did sometimes imagine) that she was being talked about, or worse, laughed at. And here she was, true to form, responding strongly to my unfortunate action of talking about her and patting her on the head.

Scene 6: 'Have you got the car?'

As we've seen, Dad's pattern was to be largely silent for much of the time, but to have confused days from time to time where he could be quite chatty, as though he were back in active life, a player again. One winter Saturday he had one of those days, chatting about 'the site' (Was he back in his work days at ICI? I wondered).

Fred, Mary and Chris are sitting in the lounge.

Fred: (looking towards the window but appearing to see something different) There's no work being done on the site…

Chris: It's Saturday.

Fred: I didn't realise I wasn't being paid for the work I'm doing here. (Pause) Have you got the car?

Chris: Yes.

Fred: You can give us a lift home.

Wondering where he means by home, Chris nods non-committally. Mary too seems to feel they are all going somewhere.

Chris: We don't have to go anywhere.

After a while it's tea time; Fred and Mary are led to the tea table. Chris goes to the table with them, ready to say goodbye and leave them to their tea. But as she prepares to go, Fred gets agitated.

Fred: Don't go yet. You need to give us a lift.

Chris: But you don't need to go anywhere. You've got a room here.

Fred: (clearly unconvinced, to Mary) We can take the bus.

Chris: (rather desperate) It's too cold.

Fred is upset. He gets up from the table. One of the Seniors is nearby.

Senior: Drink your tea, Fred.

Fred: I'm sick of drinking bloomin' tea.

Chris feels it might be better to slip away. As she goes down the corridor she hears:

Fred: Chris has gone.

Chris feels as though she's betrayed him, so she goes back.

Chris: Here I am, but I have to go now to get my own tea.

She leaves again. Fred gets up to try and follow. As she leaves she hears the Senior, very patient:

Senior: It's alright, Fred. Sit down and finish your tea.

Dad's emotions here came out of his confusion about being mentally (and emotionally) in a different time zone, at another stage of his life and needing to be somewhere. My emotions were about not being able to enter his confusion therefore having to stay in the 'real world', knowing that, at that moment, he didn't understand why. The only consolation about scenes like these is that they are forgotten very quickly. By the dementia sufferer anyway. The next time I visited Dad he had no idea he'd wanted a lift home.

I, on the other hand, didn't forget so easily. Though I knew he was operating in a different time zone, though I know I had no need to feel guilty about not 'giving him a lift home' because the home he had in mind no longer existed, I still felt Dad's agitation and distress, both then and whenever I think about the incident. 'Chris has gone', he said taking away his chance of getting where he thought he needed to go. And I felt terrible – an example of the emotional impact of Dad's dementia at that moment possibly being greater for me than for him.

Scene 7: Birthdays and anniversaries

Mum developed a mischievous sense of humour. On her 92nd birthday we had this conversation.

Chris: How old are you?

Mary: A hundred.

Chris: You know that's not true.

Mary: You have to be able to tell some lies sometimes.

With little sense of time, dates, even important ones like birthdays and wedding anniversaries, don't seem to mean anything any more. On December 23rd 2008 Fred and Mary had been married for 69 years.

Chris is sitting with Fred and Mary on that day.

Chris: (to Mary) You've been married sixty-nine years.

Mary looks surprised.

Mary: (to Fred) You never told me!

Fred looks at Chris for help – seems like he didn't know it either!

Scene 8: On Christmas Day a child visits

I visit Mum and Dad on Christmas morning and give them their presents though Mum, as we'd seen the previous Christmas, doesn't seem to understand what a present is any more. Dad falls upon his diabetic chocolates and also helps himself to some of Mum's non-diabetic chocs that look so much more inviting. The carers are doing their best to stir up a festive atmosphere but it is proving hard work.

But then a young man arrives, tall, with his young daughter, 18 months old, in his arms. They've come to visit his grandfather, her great-grandfather, a frail old man who lives on the unit and doesn't say much but smiles and waves. Dad calls him the Bunny Man because of his tendency to 'hop' around.

The little girl is shy to start with but soon gets down from her father's arms and wanders cheerfully about the residents' lounge. All eyes are upon her. Residents who can't speak smile, follow her around with their eyes. Both Mum and Dad are beaming, trying to catch her eye. For her part, the little girl is fascinated by everything, the fish in the aquarium, the wrapping paper, the old people sitting around. No judgement, just curiosity. And in response, residents who have lost much of themselves show they still have left the simple reactions of pleasure and fascination with a little child.

Scene 9: 'I could kill her'

As Dad spends so much of his time asleep, Mum often sits in the lounge companionably next to Dorothy, exchanging remarks that sometimes make sense and sometimes don't. Dorothy is younger than Mum, and seems to feel more at ease in herself if she has someone to look after. She's chosen Mum as her current protégée, something Mum doesn't seem fully to realise.

Mum and Dorothy are sitting in armchairs in the lounge side by side when Chris comes to visit. Unusually Dorothy is asleep. Mary nevertheless addresses remarks to her, getting no response.

Mary: (to Chris, indicating Dorothy) I could kill her!

Chris: (never afraid to state the obvious) She's asleep.

Mary makes angry noises and glares at the sleeping Dorothy.

I remember being surprised at Mum's vehemence at Dorothy's being asleep and therefore not responding to her remarks. Normally what Mum seemed to need from her was some kind of confirmation of whatever she was saying. But now I was there Mum could simply have switched her attention to me, but she didn't. It was as though she needed Dorothy's support to show to outsiders – me in this case – that they knew they had a life, knew what they were talking about.

Well, that was one possible explanation for Mum's strength of feeling. But then something totally different could have been going on. Did Mum believe that Dorothy was someone else, someone from her own past who seemed to be letting her down? In dementia, we cannot know for sure what triggers emotion. We can observe and we can guess. Wrongly or rightly.

Scene 10: 'Was I potty just now?'

People with Alzheimer's-style dementia can often be less inhibited than they've been in the past. When I take Mum for a walk round the home and gardens, for example, and we meet people, she's not at all shy. At least that's what I've assumed. But reflecting on it – actually it's with the carers that she is smiley and jokey and funny. She has carers she feels are her friends, and when she sees them, in her unit or outside, her face lights up.

But other residents, even if she's seen them a number of times before, she doesn't seem to register in the same way. If I'm with her and we meet one of her favourite carers, she may say to them, pointing to me: 'I'm her mother', as though this is the first time they've heard this. Even when they tell her they already know, she doesn't seem bothered. But the same isn't true of exchanges with other residents.

Chris and Mary have been for a walk around the gardens. Chris is holding Mary's hand. As they come into the building Chris greets an old lady, a resident of the 'ordinary' part of the home, who is sitting in the porch relaxing in an armchair.

Mary: (to the resident, pointing to Chris) I'm her mother.

Resident: Oh. That's nice.

Chris: We've been for a walk.

Mary: I'm her mother.

Chris and Mary go in through the door and walk down the corridor towards the Green Unit.

Mary: Was I potty, just now?

Chris: No, you were fine.

Two things I noticed from this tiny incident: one was that Mum makes a distinction between carers whom she feels relaxed with, and residents where she feels less at ease. The other was that Mum had retained that worry we all of us have occasionally: did I make a fool of myself there? Though uninhibited some of the time, she could still be self-conscious too.

Life goes on

Scenes like these take place all day and every day. Scenes of joy and sadness. Scenes of anxiety, annoyance, acceptance. If the scenes had been focused on one of the other residents, chosen by one of their relatives, then of course the detail would have been different. But there would still have been a whole range and variety of emotion.

Viewed by a one-off visitor, sitting in the lounge, sometimes sleepily, dementia sufferers can look, at first glance, like a roomful of old people who are dead to the world. But at close quarters, viewed over a longer timescale, the picture is more complex: a mix of different personalities and therefore different emotional responses, arising from different experiences, different types of dementia, different lives.

'So long as we're together, it doesn't matter at all'

In one way my Mum and Dad were different to their fellow-residents in the downstairs unit in that they were two who had shared a life and, though much depleted, continued to do so.

In that card we came across that Dad had given Mum on their Diamond Wedding Anniversary, he'd also said this: 'Maybe everything has not always gone to plan…but looking back I wouldn't have wanted to share a minute of the whole sixty years with anyone but you'.

For some reason, that phrase 'maybe everything has not always gone to plan' stuck in my mind. And came back in thinking about their situation. Living in the dementia unit of a care home, losing their minds at different rates and in different ways, was almost certainly not what they had planned.

Yet in spite of all the negatives, they enjoyed one big positive: they were together. Though fractured and fragmented, their emotional life as a couple nevertheless continued. Even when Dad became mostly silent and disappeared to his room to sleep much of the time, he still had his more expansive moments. The carers used to tell me little stories:

'The other day at breakfast, Fred appears. 'Hello, darling', he says to Mary and gives her a kiss'.

'They were in the lounge earlier after lunch sitting next to each other. They both fell asleep holding hands'.

However imperfectly I guess they were still able to give each other some emotional stability. They each had someone in their daily lives who knew them and totally accepted them as a person. They may not have been able to express themselves any more or even to help each other in many practical ways. But they could smile when they met, and they could still hold hands.

Time is not on our side

In that last conversation I had with the hospital Care Manager before Mum and Dad had come into the home, I'd said how hard it was. 'It'll get harder', she'd replied.

And she was right. I could already see that the day would come when Mary and Fred would no longer recognise each other, their love story finally over after more than 70 years.

And I could see that the day would come when one or other would no longer recognise me. Though I accept that as being inevitable, yet feel great sadness. Dementia is a disorder of the brain swimming in a sea of emotion.

Ours and theirs. Ours more lasting.

Chapter 9
The long march into silence

And so to the future. What lies ahead? No happy ending, that's for sure, though Fred and Mary's love story has one more highlight as, with a party for the whole of the care home planned, and a card from the Queen requested by me, they will celebrate their 70th wedding anniversary on 23rd December 2009. Two ordinary people who, in the length of their marriage, join the ranks of the extraordinary.

As the date approached they had been in the care home for well over two years, their dementia progressing slowly with the seasons. Fred had more or less given up walking, his muscles wasted through disuse, just enough strength left to creep, snail-like, pushing his walking frame the 20 metres or so from his room to the lounge. Except on his confused days when he seemed to regain his strength and couldn't keep still. By this time Mary had been prescribed a walking frame too but rarely used it, preferring for support to hold on to the wooden rails that run along the corridors, or the arm of a carer. Still a wanderer, she remained one of the more mobile members of her little community, though she was beginning to pay the price with some nasty falls.

I continued to visit them regularly, gradually becoming aware that maintaining regularity was more for my benefit than theirs.

If I went on holiday they didn't appear to realise I was away. Or rather, when I returned, they didn't seem aware I'd gone. Why did this surprise me? After all, I know dementia wipes out your memory, starting with the most recent, and alters your sense of time and space. Yet a side of me still expected them to react in a 'normal' way, say they were glad I was back, that they'd missed me, or ask me how my holiday was. It was as though I was still expecting them to act as proper parents and show an interest! Old expectations are hard to shift.

I'm a slow learner: it took more than two years for it to finally sink in that, because Mum has never known she's in a care home, when I visit her, she can't be experiencing it as her daughter visiting her in her care home. How could she? When I walk into the lounge, her eyes light up in recognition and I've gone on taking it for granted she's pleased I'm visiting her. Yet her eyes light up in recognition when she sees a familiar carer too. And sometimes she seems a little disconcerted when I arrive as though she's trying hard to place me, or to figure out how I've suddenly appeared.

'Where have you been?' she asked as I walked in one day that autumn, in a way that suggested I'd disappeared for no good reason, and here I was back again. Uncertain what was going on in her mind, I wasn't sure of the best response. 'I've been shopping', I tried, but 'shopping' drew a blank look from Mum, one of her favourite activities consigned to oblivion. When I visited again a few days later she was ill with a cold which befuddled her brain even more than usual. That day she clearly didn't know my name. 'I'll give you a clue', I said. 'C…R…' 'Crack', she guessed. 'No, Chris'. 'Chris', she repeated. 'That's a nice name'. 'You chose it', I said. 'You're my mother. That's why I come to see you. Make sure you're alright'.

The next time I see her, however, she definitely knows I'm part of the family. 'Where's my father?' she asks as we sit drinking tea together. She'd been getting personal pronouns mixed up for a while. Where she used to point to me and tell anyone who'd listen: 'I'm her mother', she was now as likely to tell them: 'She's my mother'. I guess, therefore, that she may actually be asking me where Dad is. 'You mean my father?' She ponders. 'Your husband? Fred?' 'Yes'. 'He's in his room'. And there's that eternal surprise again: 'Ooh, where is it?' 'Just down there. Along the corridor'.

As for Dad, two years or so after coming in I assume he still knows he's in a care home, but I can't check because he doesn't speak any more. Or hardly. Sometimes he smiles when I arrive, and sometimes he doesn't. On his better days he may utter a word or two. One day I asked him how he was and instead of his usual 'Terrible' he replied: 'So-so'. I was thrilled not just to hear him speak, but also because 'so-so' was not entirely negative. If he's feeling so-so, then he's not in despair, not so sad. And if he's not so sad, then I feel lighter too.

How much worse?

What lies ahead we don't precisely know. All we know for sure at this point is that their dementia is drawing them both downhill in their different ways. How far and how fast I can only assess by comparing this year with the one before. Dad joined Mum in the downstairs unit in the autumn of 2008. On my first visit after his move, Mum and Dad were sitting in the lounge, companionably side by side in the two armchairs visitors can see as they approach down the corridor. That day Dad was wide awake, looking jaunty in his green baseball cap. Though not making much sense he was positively chatty, wanting to buy a pair of '5 guinea glasses', bringing his old employers ICI into the conversation as well as the RAF. Mum was lively too – seeming on the point of explaining how Dad needed sorting out in some way but never quite getting it clear. Dad got restless – he could walk unaided then though he usually used a stick. He got up, crossed the room and peered behind the curtain then sat down again and put both his feet up on the side table that usually held their drinks. That was how it was then.

Compare that to a year later when I visited one day in the autumn of 2009. They were side by side in the lounge in these same armchairs. No jaunty baseball cap this time though: Dad was half lying in his armchair, one leg on the floor, the other up on that same side table, fast asleep. Mum saw me and her eyes brightened: she pummelled Dad's leg, the one up on the table, in an effort to wake him to share my arrival but his eyes remained resolutely closed. 'It's OK, leave him,' I said, so used to Dad being asleep that I was surprised when he wasn't. More often he would sleep in or on his bed; at least this way I get to see him, though during the hour or so I'm there he opens his eyes for no more than a couple of minutes. Where in the early days I used to be a comfort to him, the oblivion of sleep eventually became of far greater comfort.

Having no concept of 'visit' Mum seems to assume my arrival signals something, but she's not sure what. Nor can I guess what she's expecting. Her language is failing and though she can start sentences she rarely finishes them. Mainly she uses general words – 'What's…they…that thing…should you be…there…'. Many of the words for specifics have been wiped out of her memory. If pressed as to what she wants to say she looks blank: 'I can't remember anything'. She can say that articulately enough just as she can still express feelings. 'She's awful', she'll regularly say of one of the residents whose uninhibited behaviour continues to shock her. 'You laugh every time you see my face', says one of the Seniors. 'You've got a very nice face', Mum responds. These kinds of responses she can still make.

This is the way it is two years in. Dad silent and almost permanently asleep, Mum flailing for words that will no longer come. And yet…

Still a star

And yet, whereas Dad began his withdrawal long before coming into the home, even with worsening dementia befuddling her brain, Mum is still a player. 'Let's go for a walk', I say and she agrees, a little uncertainly as she doesn't exactly know what I'm proposing. I take her hand and we walk along the corridor towards the door with the security code that I know and she doesn't. She likes to hold hands with our fingers interlocked, until I remember the warning of one of the assistant managers. Be careful how you hold her hand, she'd said. Do it this way – and she'd shown me how to keep my thumb free, to hold Mum's hand nearer the wrist. Why? Because if she falls, she'll hold on so strongly, gripping so hard that you could end up with your thumb dislocated. I adjust our hands and go through the door out into the freer world of the ordinary residential part of the home.

Mum has fun as we run into people she recognises including the manager, big smiles and 'Hello, Marys' all round. We go down to the lounge in the other ground floor unit. And Mum's a star. It's the surprise and delight she shows when she recognises someone that moves people – in this case it's the carer on duty she's thrilled to see, and also one of the residents who was on her unit for a time. She doesn't know where she is, she can't say much, yet all eyes are upon her because, like a child, she's curious and unpredictable. After browsing around the room, she makes herself at home in one of the armchairs. Eventually I drag her away, and like a child who wants to stay a bit longer on the swings, she protests. As we go back along the corridor, the door of one of the rooms is open. Leaving Mum in the corridor for a moment I call in to say hello to a resident I know, who himself has visitors. Mum then appears in the doorway. 'Hello', says one of the visitors to Mum. 'How are you?' 'Very well, thank you', Mum replies very politely. She can remember polite phrases too, I note.

Though her dementia is decidedly worse, showing up in her deteriorating language, and in other ways, she still has plenty of personality, blooming now she has lost many of her inhibitions. She still engages with the world. At the same time I wonder if taking her out of her day-to-day environment is also disconcerting as she seems unsettled when we get back. I've certainly noticed, for instance, that some residents are more confused than usual when they return from the weekly Church Service held in the upstairs part of the home. Not Mum as she never seems to have any idea she's just been to a Church Service. But one of the others sometimes begins to wail that her husband has just died and I wonder, did the service cause her to believe she'd just been to his funeral?

On this particular day, we go back to the lounge and Mum sits down beside Dad again. He's still asleep and she soon gets restless. She goes over to the tables now set with cups and saucers for tea and starts banging a cup down on to its saucer. One of the carers tries to distract her by taking her to have a look out of the window. Normally she loves looking out but today something is making her uneasy. By now it's medication time, always a struggle, not because Mum refuses the painkillers meant to help her arthritic knees, but because she's forgotten the process of swallowing down a pill with a glass of water. So instead she chews the pill while the rest of us, me and the carers, try to discourage her: 'Ugh, no Mary that tastes horrible, swallow it down.' But like 'shopping', the word 'swallow' appears to mean nothing to Mum any more. So she keeps chewing, not appearing to object to the taste. 'Has it gone, Mary?' Mum opens her mouth obediently, and the pill, sucked smaller, is still there. 'Here, drink this…' And so it goes on till the pill finally disappears.

It's tea time now and the residents are helped to the table. Being mobile Mum gets there quickly and is encouraged to sit down. But with no apparent idea of what she's doing at the table, she gets up again and wanders off. Dad arrives and sits next to her but this doesn't help. 'Sit down, Mary. Have your tea'. I slip away in case my presence is making things worse. 'Sit down, Mary' – the words waft after me down the corridor as I tap in the security code that takes me back into the non-demented world.

Compassionate concern

Though at this point we don't know what the future holds and how their ends will play out – whether dementia will carry Mum off when she can no longer remember how to eat or drink or even breathe, or whether she or Dad will have a sudden stroke or heart attack – we are relieved they are in good hands. One of the benefits of both of them being on the downstairs unit is that staff keep a very close eye on them. The regular staff in particular know them well and soon notice if they are not themselves. The care home is close to where they used to live which also means they've stayed registered with the same GP surgery I got to know so well when they were still living at home. The surgery seems to have taken on more proactive staff too, judging by the different doctors who ring me to discuss decisions about Mum and Dad's medical care.

Medicine these days is essentially test-based with GPs the gatekeepers for hospital investigations into symptoms reported by patients or anomalies thrown up by routine blood tests. One such blood test showed that Mum was anaemic: a doctor I hadn't spoken to before rang to discuss the next step. Mum's kind of anaemia, she explained, wasn't one they could simply treat by giving more iron. To investigate further would mean invasive tests...the question was should we put Mum through these tests, given her age, her dementia and the fact that she didn't have obvious symptoms. No, we shouldn't was my gut response, which chimed with the doctor's. The best course, we agreed, was to keep a watching eye for further symptoms to see if our decision should need to be revised. I was grateful to this doctor for her common sense and compassionate concern.

Playing safe

Dad has had a more mixed experience with the medical system. Though he sleeps much of the time, this is 'ordinary sleep', sleep from which he can be wakened and encouraged to get up for lunch or tea. From time to time, however, he has days, or sometimes a couple of days, when he sleeps so resolutely that he refuses to be wakened. His eyes might flicker open if anyone tries hard to wake him but immediately close again. And if they persist in trying to drag him out of sleep, he can get quite aggressive.

We were away and Alan was visiting the home when Dad was in one of these extreme sleep states. Though the home had seen him like this before, they were nevertheless worried and had called in the GP. The doctor didn't know what to make of Dad's state and decided to play safe by having him checked out at the hospital. Alan went up with him, not necessarily expecting him to be admitted. It wasn't obvious what was wrong so the hospital too played safe and admitted him to one of the old people's wards. Apparently, in his determination to remain asleep, he fought two male nurses who tried to take his clothes off and get him into a hospital gown!

As part of the intake procedure, Alan was asked if Dad should be resuscitated if his heart stopped (a standard question, I understand, rather than because they thought this would happen). The doctor suggested that with Dad's dementia and poor quality of life the answer should be no. Upset by the speed at which things were moving – from 'perhaps the hospital should take a look at him' to 'we don't think he should be resuscitated' – Alan thought he'd disagreed with the doctor, but when I saw Dad's notes a few days later they did indeed say 'DNR' 'Do Not Resuscitate', reasons given, dementia and poor quality of life. The reasons were perfectly correct, of course. It was the starkness, laying bare the fact that the medical system didn't judge his to be a life worth fighting for, that sent a surge of grief though my body.

Being a DNR patient did not mean, however, that the hospital were half-hearted in their medical treatment. On the contrary, they tested Dad from head to toe. Admitted on a Thursday evening, and booked in for various tests on the Friday, Dad's stay then ran into the weekend, when not much testing goes on. He was therefore kept in for more tests on Monday and Tuesday, none of which indicated anything much more than dehydration. His medical care could not be faulted, and he came out well rehydrated, but I saw with 20/20 clarity how a hospital ward is the worst place in the world for an old person with dementia. Hospitals are busy places; old people with dementia are slow and confused. They can't explain their own needs or understand what is happening to them. Moderate dementia can, as a result, become severe. In my opinion each demented old person who finds themselves in hospital needs a champion, just as children often have a parent with them for comfort and to interpret their needs. I hated Dad being there, and was fearful he could die there, and so was mightily relieved when he was declared medically fit for discharge.

When he finally got back to the home he was, reportedly, delighted to see his room again. But I was left with that terrible dread of him ever having to go back into hospital: I simply couldn't bear it if he were to die under the bright lights and brisk impersonality of one of those old people's wards.

Keeping him comfortable

A couple of months or so later, Dad had another of his unwakeable days. I was there – it was the first time I'd seen him in this state. Given the fact that last time the hospital hadn't found anything wrong beyond dehydration, I agreed with the Senior on duty that they'd try to get some fluid into him, and keep a watching eye. Next day he was back to normal sleeping. A week later, however, the same thing happened again and this time the home did call the GP. I was walking into town when she called me to talk about Dad, another of the new doctors I hadn't spoken to before with a tinge of Australian in her accent.

I sat down in the sunshine to have my discussion with her. How aggressively (that's the word I remember but I could be wrong, she may have used a different one), she wanted to know, did we want them to investigate Dad's unwakeable states? 'I don't want him going back into hospital', I said, not quite answering the question. It was the first thought that came to my mind. Don't let them take him away.

'If he was younger and this was happening, I'd definitely want him looked at in hospital', she said. 'But given his age and his history...' I repeated that I hated the idea of his going into hospital. He's more confused there...Of course, if it were an emergency, if he was in great pain...I suddenly realised I couldn't reasonably rule out hospital in any circumstances. The doctor was gentle in her response: if he were in pain for any reason, we could deal with that. He wouldn't need to go into hospital. 'You mean he could stay in the home whatever happens?' 'We could put in his notes that he should be kept comfortable'.

'I'm not saying he's going to die', she added. 'He could live for another couple of years. Or more'. What we were agreeing was that if he were ill, he'd be kept comfortable, and treated locally if that were possible, but he wouldn't be subjected to hospital examinations or investigations. If they put that in his notes, then the home would know how to proceed. Another kind of DNR, I suppose, but one that gave me a huge sense of relief.

Falling about

As a result of these various medical encounters, the future for both of them looked set fair to be a policy of 'minimum intervention' in which they'd be looked after in the home, kept comfortable so that, if they did get ill, they'd be in familiar surroundings with people they knew, and, more importantly I realised after Dad's stay in hospital, with people who knew them.

What I didn't reckon with was Mum and Dad's tendency to have accidents. Early one morning we were woken by the phone – it was one of the night carers letting me know that Mum had got up very early but had then fallen hitting her face and was on her way to hospital. It took a good couple of weeks for the bruises on her face to fade. A few weeks later I had a call to let me know that Dad had hit his head during the night or in the early morning. No-one quite knew how he'd done it but the result was a big swelling under his eye and an enormous bruise.

I don't know why Mum and Dad seemed to be more accident prone than their fellow residents. This wasn't Mum's first bad fall. In her case I guess that incessant wandering plus unwillingness to use a walking frame made falling more likely. And Dad? Who knows?

And me?

That's how they were in the autumn of 2009 as they entered their third year in the home. A precarious present, an edging into silence. For Dad the silence of sleep. For Mum the silence of words forgotten.

And me? How was I? Much relieved and less burdened is what first comes to mind. I could breathe again and live my life more normally. Sad too, particularly when I felt Dad's continuing despair. And a little guilty sometimes that I actually began to find it easier to visit when he was asleep. I didn't always wake him as I knew that on waking he would take a good while to come to, or he'd open his eyes briefly then close them again. I guess I was relieved I wouldn't have to feel the pain of seeing how he was suffering at still being in the world.

Or that's how it looked. But I must remember I was only guessing. I could have been wrong. I visited one day when Dad was asleep, that was the day I became aware that I felt relieved, but then later, when he got himself up for tea, he was soft and smiley and actually spoke as he sat down: 'I need a shave', he said seeming remarkably matter-of-fact.

As he'd walked slowly towards the lounge pushing his frame

along the corridor, Mum had been by the door, and they'd greeted each other with pleasure. The moment didn't last long as they both went off into their own worlds, but the spark was still there, the love story not completely over.

I still feel anxiety, especially as I observe Mum's brain worsen, but I feel richer too for having spent this time so close to my parents. A time of intimacy which is a gift. The part of the home where they live, a unit of only eleven residents, has an intimate feel as the people who live there struggle with the very basics of life: Who am I? Where am I? No more pretence: they are who they are now, silent or noisy, anxious or cheerful, ignoring each other or relating. I feel privileged to be part of their present, hard though it is for them. Not just Mum and Dad but the others too. I've learnt a lot – may it serve me well in my own ageing.

Chapter 10

Love story: the grand finale?

In my parents' marriage Dad had been the Romantic and Mum the Realist. As a product of their genes I am a Realist/Romantic, the Realist side stronger just as my Mum was the stronger partner in their relationship. But, like her, I have a Romantic streak too. I guess it was my Romantic side that pushed me into believing that Dad and Mum's love story was not entirely over, that their love would endure 'till death do them part'.

Perhaps then it was my Romantic streak that urged me, in June 2009, to mention to the manager of Mum and Dad's care home, during the annual review of their care, that on 23rd December they would be celebrating their 70th wedding anniversary. Their Platinum Anniversary, I later learnt 70 years wed is called. Not many people know its name as not many reach that milestone.

I didn't have to draw attention to it but I guess I was proud of their achievement. I felt it made them special. Yet I was also Realist enough to realise that by that December one of them or both might not be in good enough mental shape to understand what they had achieved. After all, the year before they'd both been hazy about their 69th anniversary. Would a round figure really make such a difference?

The manager, however, was very positive seeing a Platinum Wedding Anniversary as definitely an event worth celebrating. They'd have a party for the whole home, she said. At this point December still seemed a long way away off.

The Queen

In the autumn she gave me information on how to get Mum and Dad a Platinum Anniversary card sent from the Queen. Some people think the Queen somehow 'knows' when one of her subjects reaches 100 years old, or a couple celebrate their 70th Wedding Anniversary. But actually to get a card from the Queen there is a system, a form to be filled out and sent to the Anniversaries Office at Buckingham Palace. Relatives are asked to wait till the anniversary date is no more than three weeks away before sending in the form, presumably because not everyone makes that last lap.

I was uneasy though, aware as the months rolled by that mentally both Dad and Mum were moving steadily downhill. Suppose the home organised a big party and neither Mum nor Dad had any idea what was going on. Or, even worse, what if on 23rd December Dad had one of those 'won't wake up' days. I didn't share my fears, or at least not many of them, and Mum and Dad's Anniversary Party went into the home's calendar.

The manager was upbeat and reassuring: 'Mary'll recognise the Queen on the card, won't she?' Actually I couldn't even be sure of that, remembering the way Mum had sung 'God save our gracious King' on her first Christmas in the home. I wasn't even clear if it was morally right to put on a party for people who weren't able to say whether they wanted such a celebration. For their Diamond Anniversary ten years ago, when they were both perfectly compos mentis, they, or rather, Mum hadn't wanted any fuss so we kept it away from the local paper and strictly in the family. And yet Mum and Dad were always surprising me these days. What harm could it do? I decided. A chance for the whole home to have some fun. 'It'll be a nice occasion for you to remember,' the manager said. Mmm. Alan is not even going to be there, I learn. He and Sue have decided to spend Christmas in their house in Cyprus this year. I'll have to be the 'responsible adult' again.

As the day drew closer I dutifully filled in the Buckingham Palace form enclosing a copy of their marriage certificate which I'd spent hours searching for among their papers. I'd about given up when I opened a small envelope containing two flimsy 92 year old birth certificates and, there finally in black and white: their marriage certificate. Frederick Carling to Mary Davis. Both 22, occupations 'Clerk', she living in Billingham with her parents, he living with his in Cowpen Bewley. They were married in Billingham Parish Church by the Vicar, Mr Timms.

I started to look out pictures of their wedding, working through the piles of photos from the past that I'd stuffed away in a carrier bag to 'sort out later'. Magically those wartime days came to life. Here was Fred in his RAF uniform, flight training in Canada and Florida; a Christmas mess card he'd sent Mary in 1942 giving the Christmas Day menu, and all his love wishing she was here. Here was Mary with her sisters and her friends, Mary posing demurely at her comptometer. Mum and Dad before they became my parents.

The young couple were married on 23rd December 1939, their marriage brought forward, as were many, because of the outbreak of war. Why wait when Hitler threatened and Fred might be called up any time? Mary looked stunning in her white slim line satin wedding dress, her face framed by a light lace veil. Realist even then to Fred's Romantic, she'd intended, when their marriage was brought forward, to make it a simple affair saying she'd just wear a smart suit. It was her father, my grandfather who died before I was born, who insisted she have a long white dress and a 'proper wedding'.

How will the Big Day be?

My plan is to create a display of photographs and mementoes to put up in the home on the Big Day. And so, for a time, I bury myself in the past, bringing Mum and Dad's milestones to life, scanning in photos of Mum as a bride, Dad as a groom. I try shopping for a Platinum Wedding Anniversary card but find none later than Diamond. 60 years, yes, there's a demand. But 70 years married – sorry, no market. No 'Happy 70th Wedding Anniversary!' banner either, so I settle for a 'Happy Anniversary' banner and add the number.

At the same time, as December rolls by, I'm aware that both Mum and Dad are deteriorating fast. Dad is restless when he's up. When he's not asleep he can't settle. He makes to get up, to go somewhere. 'Where do you want to go, Dad?' 'I don't know', he says in some desperation. When he sees me he gives a smile but that's all.

And Mum too – she seems to be smiling and laughing less. She can't get her words out at all. We're sitting together and Dad shuffles over led by a carer. 'Here's Fred,' I say but Mum doesn't seem to 'see' him. I point to him but it's still as if she looks but can't see.

It seems they both need the limited amount of energy they have left to cope with themselves. Have they nothing left now for each other? The Romantic in me persists in wondering if there will be a last spark. Inspired by the day on which they'll have been 70 years wed? 23rd December 2009.

Even my Realist side acknowledges this is a possibility. The strength of the human spirit can surprise us all. In the meantime I do my stuff. The manager asks me to put together some information for the local paper, the Cambridge News. We both agree we don't want a photographer round to take their picture. I can just imagine how awful it would be, a journalist asking them those questions they always ask the long married: what's your secret? What's kept you together all this time? Neither of them being able to respond. Instead I scan in a fairly recent photo and we email the information.

In my conscientious way I'm trying to do all I can to make the occasion as good as it can be. Their moment of glory. But I worry about how it's actually going to be on the Big Day. Is the reality that their long partnership is already over? No, not yet, my Romantic says. Not while they still have some spirit left. 'Everyone with dementia is capable of a moment of lucidity', an Alzheimer's Society spokesperson I saw on TV a few days before had said. Let's hope Mum and Dad have some lucid moments on 23rd December! Just so long as Dad doesn't have one of his 'won't wake up' days.

How it was

The evening before the Big Day I receive a call from the home: had anyone told me that Dad had fallen that morning? No, they hadn't. He'd hit his nose, they say. A nurse had come and put on a dressing. Great, I thought. Dad will celebrate his Platinum Wedding Anniversary with a dressing on his nose. Dad's OK, I'm told, though a bit shaken up.

On the Day itself I get to the home at about 9.30 am. The card from Buckingham Palace is there. That's the positive. 'Dad's not very well', the manager says. That's the negative. At this point I don't know how 'not very well' he is. One of the assistant managers helps me put together my photos on a big display board. I'm proud of the result, showing, as it does, Mum and Dad as a vibrant happy couple, not just on their wedding day but on their Golden Wedding Anniversary too. I've also included that card Dad had sent to Mum on their Diamond Anniversary: an eloquent declaration of his long-lived love for her. I wanted to show how much he'd cared even though he can't express much now.

Taking the Royal Card for Mum to open I go along to the downstairs unit accompanied by the manager. Mum and Dad are both in the lounge but while Mum is alert Dad is decidedly not. He's in a wheelchair, lying back, mouth open, completely out of it. Not only is he not waking up (oh no, surely this isn't going to be one of his 'won't wake up' days), his hand and wrist are badly swollen where he fell yesterday. The doctor has been called and there is talk of Dad perhaps having to go to Addenbrooke's to have his hand X-rayed. The day is taking on a dreadful hue. The carers on duty wheel Dad back to his room where he resolutely goes to sleep.

Back in the lounge Mum is the centre of attention, the card from the Queen a big hit. She may not know exactly what it's for but she's certainly impressed, opening and re-opening it, intrigued by the 'ElizabethR' signature and the 'Mr and Mrs Frederick Carling' in the bottom left hand corner. 'That's you and Fred', I tell her. Who knows what she understands?

I present my gifts: a tall pink orchid and a box of Swiss chocolates, then there are more family cards to open, none as imposing as the one from the Queen but they make a fine display. I'd bought a card for Dad to give her and, it turns out, yesterday a carer helped him write 'To Mary' and his name 'Fred'. Even that was a struggle for him, she said. But he did it all the same. A tiny spark?

As Mum shows off her cards to everyone who comes by, I dart between the lounge and Dad's room, willing him to wake up. But he just goes on snoring. Loudly. Mum, I notice, doesn't ask where he is.

I face the fact that my worst fears are being realised: Dad is having one of his 'won't wake up' days. Today. On their 70th Wedding Anniversary. When he is supposed to be on show beside Mum. But worse still is the prospect of the doctor, when he arrives, wanting him up at the hospital having his hand X-rayed in A&E. When Dad 'won't wake' it's very hard to move him – and experience has shown that if he's left to sleep, then next day he's likely to be back to normal. He's definitely better off where he is, I decide, and make it my mission to keep him here where he's warm, safe and secure. To keep him away from hospital. For that I need to wait for the doctor's visit. So I wait, and wait as Mum continues to inspect her Royal Card and Dad snores on.

Eventually the doctor arrives, a pleasant young man who takes a look at Dad in his 'won't wake up' state, notes his swollen hand (which is looking a bit better): 'We'll get him X-rayed in A&E', he says as an opening gambit, 'and they can take a more general look at him'. 'I don't think that's a very good idea', I reply immediately in my role of defender. The young doctor is slightly taken aback but he listens to me. In my favour is the result of Dad's blood sugar test which is not alarming. The doctor then examines Dad's hand himself thoroughly enough to assess that though bruised there is nothing broken. He repeats that Dad's thumb is definitely not broken several times, explaining that if it had been he would have had no choice but to send him up to the hospital. As it is he's listening to my story, that Dad has these 'won't wake' days, that he's been up to Addenbrooke's and they didn't find any obvious reason, that he's better off being allowed to sleep on where he is. The doctor offers some ideas about modifying Dad's diabetes medication, leaves with a urine sample the carers have managed to get earlier, and agrees to Dad being left alone. Hooray! Mission completed.

It's well after lunch by now. The Party is scheduled for a 5 pm buffet tea followed by an entertainer in the upstairs lounge at 6 pm, with sherry and cutting the special anniversary cake. I go off for a couple of hours to pick up on my non-anniversary life, visiting my god-children to deliver their Christmas presents. I'm hoping for a miracle: perhaps by the time I get back, Dad will be awake.

But he isn't. Instead one of the assistant managers has to spend half an hour coaxing half a cup of liquid into him so he doesn't get too dehydrated. The party organisers wonder if it would be possible to get him into a wheelchair so at least he's physically present next to Mum. But it's just not going to happen.

He's completely out of it – in one of those states where, if anyone tries too hard to force him awake, he is liable to hit out.

And so, the buffet tea eaten, the downstairs unit residents, minus Dad, assemble with the rest of the home in the upstairs lounge. Mum is guest of honour. My photographic display has been brought up from the entrance hall and occupies centre stage. We admire the cake. Everyone is there, even residents who are normally confined to bed. Except Dad. Except one of the key players.

And so we wait. And wait. A message comes from the singer, Dave, who is supported in his act by his wife, Ann, that they are still ten minutes away. This has been a week of extreme weather with ice and snow paralysing the country: it turns out they had a lunchtime gig and got stuck on the M11 getting back. But they do finally arrive as sherry is being drunk and cake munched. Dave is a big man with long curly hair, his wife Ann short and dumpy, neither seem to have dressed up for the occasion. 'He's not very handsome, is he', says Mum in the front row. This is before he starts performing.

But Dave turns out to be a gem, well worth waiting for. Good looking he may not be, but his voice is warm and embracing, and his manner is just perfect. He handles the presence of Mum and the absence of Dad with consummate professionalism, speaking directly to Mum, explaining to the audience that Fred's not very well and is therefore staying in his room. He pays attention to Mum in the gentlest way, getting her to respond. 'Mary, I'm not sure if I can ask you this, but how old were you when you met Fred?' 'Seventeen', I prompt quietly. 'Seventeen', says Mum and Dave then adapts the song 'She was only sixteen' to 'She was only seventeen'. Ann is lovely too, taking round a mike so residents can sing into it as Dave performs love songs, Christmas songs, old time songs. I have huge fun singing along. Mum's friend, Dorothy on my left knows every word, and Mum joins in too when she can remember.

And so I'm left feeling that on balance the day has gone well considering that one of the major players was absent. Yet I'm also aware that Mum doesn't seem to have wondered why Dad wasn't there to celebrate their Big Day.

And so I guess the love story is over. There was no final spark. On their 70th Wedding Anniversary Dad was completely out of it. And Mary didn't seem to notice he wasn't there.

Definitely over, I conclude. Must be.

Next day

I wake up in the night worrying about Dad but calls from the home next day are upbeat: Fred's up and about, back to 'normal' and sitting with Mary, I'm told. He's eaten as if he's been starving for weeks and is drinking one cup of tea after another. But he's back and sitting next to Mum.

And so I revise my conclusion, making it more tentative. Their love story is not over till it's over, I decide. Till death do them part, says my Romantic side. Till even more severe dementia do them part, my Realist thinks more likely.

Epilogue

Dad died nearly a year later on 20th November 2010. A whisker after midnight. A peaceful death. A quiet death. I had been determined to keep him out of hospital and succeeded. The doctor saw his end coming and simply prescribed he should be kept comfortable.

To me Dad's dying seemed sudden. After a bout of shingles he'd been sleeping most of the time and barely eating. But we'd been here before. Then, on the morning of 19th November, a call from the home: perhaps you'd better come.

Our little family gathered. We held his hand as staff gently moistened his mouth as he could no longer drink. We told him we loved him – I don't know if he heard, but hearing is the last of our senses to go. Or so they say. We did all we could to make sure my Dad spent his last hours of life surrounded by love.

The one absent figure was his wife. Mum had no idea what was going on and we didn't tell her. She didn't enquire why we were all there that evening. We didn't take her to the funeral.

As the Realist in me had predicted, dementia did finally part these two long-time lovers, in spite of their 70 years wed. In some ways it has been a blessing: neither was truly widowed. Neither has had to grieve the other or endure the loneliness of loss.

Mum remains cheerful even though she has lost her mobility and most of her language. She's still a player, still curious, unaware probably that no-one can understand her.

And Dad is at peace, his ashes scattered beneath a hawthorn bush back up North, high on a hill in the Country Park created on the site of the Cowpen Bewley cottage where he was born. For his final resting place, we took him home.

Frederick Carling: 23rd August 1917 – 20th November 2010

Mary Carling: 2nd February 1917 –

BUT THEN SOMETHING HAPPENED

A Story of Everyday Dementia

Part 2

Standing Back

Chapter 11
The back story: why didn't we see it coming?

Dementia raises many questions not least the ones you ask yourself. Foremost for me, looking back over these past few dementia-dominated years: why didn't we see it coming? Why were we not better prepared? Mum and Dad were catapulted from muddlers-along at home to care home residents during a six-week drama that occurred one summer. But we knew that dementia does not set in overnight. That summer was not the beginning of the story. We knew that too. Dr Dening had diagnosed Dad with a vascular dementia a full year before, at that same time observing informally that Mum seemed to be in 'the early stages of Alzheimer's'. You might think, therefore, that we would have been alert, ready, prepared for things to fall apart.

But we weren't. On the contrary. We were taken totally by surprise.

How could this be?

How could this be given that the signs of growing dementia were there in both of them though in very different ways? How was it we didn't recognise these signs for what they were? Realise where they were heading? There's no single answer, I've concluded. Our heads were in the sand for many reasons.

Change came gradually, that was the main factor. I was a regular visitor and first line helper but still only saw part of the picture. Dad's diagnosis of 'vascular dementia' was just a label to start with. For all practical purposes he continued in the low, depressed state he had suffered for some while. Showing itself as 'not doing' – not saying much, not taking initiatives – vascular dementia can look like depression in the early stages. But Dad still seemed to inhabit the same world as me, he could tell fantasy from reality. As for Mum, though she did show some odd behaviour – with hindsight, quite a lot of odd behaviour, which became even odder with time – her spirit, determination and strong will meant that she could appear more normal than she almost certainly was. What is normal, after all?

Yes, each new incident made it clearer that something was definitely wrong, but in between were periods of apparent calm when Dad still joked and Mum seemed closer to her usual self. Or maybe our idea of her 'usual self' was shifting to accommodate her new behaviour.

Another factor may also have contributed: Mum and Dad were very good at putting on a convincing front. Good enough for us to take them at face value, accepting what they wanted to show us when we visited. We didn't know the full story of their day-to-day deterioration. Not until it was well advanced anyway.

Perhaps too our heads were in the sand because we didn't want to recognise what was happening to our parents' minds. I found it less painful to deal with short-term symptoms – take over tea-making, for instance, when eventually Mum couldn't remember how – than to follow through to the source and fully recognise that if Mum could no longer make a cup of tea this was likely to be because she was losing her mind. I was protecting myself, I see now. Coping with symptoms was manageable: I could take over tasks Mum and Dad could no longer do, and we would get by. Dealing with the present was demanding enough without asking why, thereby bringing in an uncertain future.

Maybe we also closed our eyes because we didn't know what to do: because if we had followed through there was no clear way ahead. Mum minus her marbles was uncharted territory; Dad couldn't help much as he had his own mental problems. We simply didn't know the script. Our experience with 'the system' had been mixed to say the least. The doctors didn't seem to know much. So who did know? Not us, that was for sure.

The wonders of hindsight

It's taken till now, telling Mum and Dad's story, for me to stand back and see more clearly. To answer my own question – why didn't we see it coming? – I need to go back a little further and take a closer look at the run-up period to Mum and Dad both going into residential care.

Difficult: that's what I remember most about the two years or so leading up to that Crisis Weekend in July 2007. I was in a fog I realise now. No wonder I couldn't see the direction of the road we were all travelling. I had my head down coping with each step on our journey, blind to our final destination.

My own diary entries didn't start till those dramatic few weeks that led to Mum and Dad both going into the home. To talk about the run-up period, which only became a run-up period with hindsight, I have to rely on memory. Though the lines are clear, the details and exact timings are blurred. But if we go back a couple of years before the breakdown of Fred and Mary as a self-sustaining couple, to 2005 when Mum and Dad were both 88, this is when the signs that marked their mental decline definitely start to show.

2005: a time of contraction

A time of contraction: that was 2005. Contraction for both Dad and Mum. Dad was turning in on himself more and more, sleeping to muffle his despair. And when he was awake he floated on massive waves of anxiety that came crashing down as he fretted about what he was no longer capable of doing.

Anxiety, now that was a sign, a brightly coloured neon sign that I only half noticed. It wasn't just the house falling down he was anxious about. Money tortured him as he became convinced their finances too were about to self-destruct. My strategy, I now see with hindsight, was to focus on the symptoms, the particular problems he was anxious about, not the source: his awareness that he was no longer capable of managing whether it was the family finances or running the house. His awareness that his mind wasn't working properly any more. I therefore offered lots of help and reassurance. And when my 'don't worry, it's fine' assurances didn't seem to be helping, I offered more.

In fairness to myself I had reason to be reassuring. The house was in reasonable shape and the household finances were not falling apart. Dad had been very sensible and far-sighted: long ago while still functioning normally he'd put all their bills on Direct Debit, so everything necessary did get paid.

Getting lost?

Mum's world also contracted due to a big milestone in early 2005 when Dad stopped driving. In the days when they were managing independently, their habit had been to go into town, look around and do some shopping. Dad had withdrawn from these trips, but while he was still driving he'd drop Mum off then go and pick her up at an appointed spot a couple of hours later. Though he was still a good driver, his 'I'm an old man and old men shouldn't drive' approach made him uneasy behind the wheel. He'd wanted to give up the car for some time, but Mum wouldn't let him. She, who had never driven, couldn't see why he couldn't carry on. 'We've always had a car', she said as though that settled it.

Eventually though Dad insisted he was hanging up his driving gloves. Mum loved going out and still wanted to go shopping so she took to walking over to the Grafton Centre, a shopping mall about ten minutes away from their house by the shortest route which involved crossing a busy road. We used to chat about her outings. From odd remarks I had the impression she was taking a roundabout route.

Concerned for her safety now that Dad stayed at home, I would question her, wanting reassurance she was taking the safest route, the one with the lights-controlled pedestrian crossing over the busy road. But these conversations were always inconclusive. She couldn't tell me in any straightforward way where she went. Her answers were puzzlingly vague.

I realise now that this inability to describe her route was one of the early signs of Mum's dementia. She could get to the Grafton Centre but couldn't say how. And she got there, I eventually figured, taking a longer and more hazardous route – she crossed the busy road where there were no pedestrian lights – because this took her to where Dad used to drop her off and pick her up. It was as though her body knew that way but her mind no longer knew what it was she knew.

Like Dad's anxiety, it was a sign I half noticed in that I was worried and tried to find out the facts, yet I didn't follow through and ask myself: what's going on in Mum's brain such that she can't tell me which way she goes, doesn't remember the names of the streets any more or which of the paths across the common she takes? So long as she managed to get there and back, I put my worries on the back burner. Or was it my head in the sand?

As the year wore on she'd occasionally worry Dad by staying out for hours though she always managed to find her way back in the end. People with Alzheimer's, I later learnt, often get lost in familiar

places. I guess she was maybe lost for a time then recovered her
sense of where she was. Dad never rang me to let me know, probably
because his own mind was slowing and taking any initiative was a
struggle. Instead he must have sat and worried on his own. Another
part of their lives where we never knew the full story.

There were other signs too but since none were dramatic they
were easy to push to the back of my mind. Mum read various
magazines, such as 'Bella', 'Best' and the Saga magazine. Old
copies would lie about and she would pick them up and read out
headlines from the cover page. 'Have you seen this?' Yes we had,
often many times. Dad would get irritated as, no doubt, she'd read
them out to him as he said, 'a thousand times'.

Or she'd be convinced she'd seen an article in a newspaper
that she wanted to show us, and take ages hunting for it. On one
occasion she leafed through magazine after magazine searching
for an advert which included a photo she thought looked like my
brother, Alan. Or that's what I assumed until I realised she thought
it actually was a photo of Alan. Another sign her mind was playing
strange tricks. Another sign to push away.

One reason I only half noticed these signs was that I was
already playing the role of go-between for my parents, the role
that came to the fore when they went into the home. My energy
was therefore fully absorbed picking my way across an emotional
minefield as Dad would be getting impatient, saying: 'No-one's
interested', and Mum would be looking hurt, so I would pretend
to be interested as she carried on searching, while trying to be
sympathetic to Dad's impatience. No wonder I didn't see the
bigger picture.

2006: help clearly needed

Obvious with hindsight, by 2006 signs of confusion were multiplying.
As it was I let them rumble in the background, continuing to respond
instead to the problems they caused by expanding my rescuer role

and upping my number of visits. My focus at this point was on keeping Mum and Dad going physically by taking care of practical chores. That in itself took up lots of time and energy, which may be another reason why I noted but nevertheless did not dwell on signs of their mental confusion and decline.

I'd gone over once a week to visit Mum and Dad when they were still fully independent. This now grew to three or more visits with all kinds of chores in between. Time spent on my professional consulting and coaching work contracted as the hours spent looking after Mum and Dad expanded. Their welfare began to sit on my shoulders as a weight that grew steadily heavier. I'd taken them on voluntarily but once they were sitting there, they were always on my mind. I'd run into a friend. 'How are you?' 'OK, though my parents aren't too good…' And I'd be off, my anxiety showing up in wanting to talk to all and sundry about my latest Mum and Dad problem.

Odd that: they were always on my mind, I was becoming a Mum-and-Dad bore, yet I still didn't clearly see what was happening. What I did see was that daily life for all of us was becoming more of a struggle. 2006 was therefore the year I decided it was time to get my parents some outside help. In the past they'd always taken a proudly independent view that went something like: 'We're old people and nobody (from 'the system') comes to see if we're OK. But actually we are OK, and we don't need any help. We can manage perfectly well by ourselves, thank you very much'. Mum still held that view but Dad, with his greater awareness of his failing body and mind, was definitely wavering towards wanting some support.

Beginning to bicker

This contrast was typical, reflecting the very different attitudes they had adopted to growing old which led to very different attitudes to their own capabilities. Dad was the one who had long been aware of the figures: 'I'm 85 (or 86, or 87...) therefore an old man', he reasoned. And if he was an old man that meant, automatically, that he couldn't do as much as before. For him the next logical step was that he was becoming useless. Mum, on the other hand, simply ignored old age. She never thought of herself as old and certainly not useless, and, in her advanced dementia, still doesn't.

As a result of these contrasting attitudes to getting old, however, they had begun to bicker. In the early days of their mental decline, being a Daddy's girl, I used to side with Dad, thinking Mum should leave him alone. Interestingly, again with hindsight, Mum also felt Dad's personality had changed: previously easy-going he would get irritated at her nagging, especially as she would try to stop him sleeping so much during the day. 'He shouts at me', she complained.

What's clear now is she saw signs before we did that Dad's mind was affected. Her way had always been to invent explanations for things she didn't understand, and to stick to these explanations doggedly. This was before dementia accentuated this tendency, causing her to confabulate. To explain changes in Dad, she became convinced he had Alzheimer's, and kept saying so. Historically my way of responding to Mum's explanations was to argue with them. And so, true to form, instead of engaging with the signs she'd observed of changes in Dad, I put my energies into insisting he didn't have Alzheimer's. Couldn't she see he was depressed? It was only later I wondered if her frequent references to Alzheimer's came from worries she already had about herself.

Consulting the experts

This was the background against which in early spring 2006 I made my initial efforts to get them some help at home. At that point I knew very little about Social Services or 'care plans' but using the County Council website as a guide, I saw that my first step should be to ask for an assessment. I put it to Dad and he agreed, saying he felt in need of help, though when I asked what in particular he wanted help with, he wasn't so sure. That was the problem. At some level we were aware that things were going downhill, but couldn't quite see what would make them better. When I asked Mum, however, she said definitely not. She didn't need help. In fact neither of them did, she claimed, but I went ahead anyway referring only Dad not Mum. 'As long as it's clear it's only him. It's nothing to do with me', Mum said when she heard the social worker was coming for the assessment visit.

The social worker was pleasant if somewhat brisk, asking questions about how Dad was managing in different areas of his day-to-day life, cooking, eating, washing, dressing and so on. In social work terms these fall into the category of 'independent living skills'. Help in this area is 'personal care'.

As we also saw later when he went into the home, the trouble was that Dad could look after himself, after a fashion. He was unmotivated and depressed but he could still function. His feeling he needed help was a more generalised 'life is too hard, I can't cope', rather than a particular 'I can't do x'. And a general feeling that you're too old to cope and that life is hard work doesn't lead a social worker to assess that you need help with 'personal care.'

We received a copy of the official Social Services report with its recommendation which essentially said Dad didn't need a care plan: 'Although Mr Carling's independent living skills appear to have deteriorated recently, he doesn't meet the criteria for care support, however he was given the Adult Care Services in Cambridgeshire booklet 2006 to consider should he and his family wish to use a private agency.' Mum was put down as Dad's carer which was ironic given what we were soon to discover about Mum's own failing mental health.

The report also noted that 'Mr Carling said he would like some assistance with washing and dressing'. I guess essentially she was saying: he's getting by, but if his relatives want to buy in some care we've given them the information. It was also noted that Mum was 'suffering from some short-term memory issues', showing that signs of Mum's dementia were clear to an outsider even though we were not giving them much attention. But Mum was not the social worker's responsibility. Dad was the 'client' I had referred to Social Services. Any observation about Mum was purely incidental.

The Older People's Mental Health Team

The social worker had noted but did not otherwise act on Mum's memory problems. She did take some action in the mental health domain, however, by referring Dad to the Older People's Mental Health Team to get some help with his constant sleeping and low spirits. It was as a result of this referral that Jane, the very helpful Community Psychiatric Nurse (CPN), mentioned in Chapter 1, came into our lives for a few months. She too could see that Mum had mental health problems of her own, but again this was just an incidental observation. Dad was her patient. He was where her responsibility began and ended.

After a few visits, Jane felt that Dad's mental state didn't quite fit a straightforward diagnosis of depression. That's when she called in the local consultant psychiatrist specialising in older people. I'd wanted to be present when Dr Dening visited but he came unannounced so I was only able to speak to him on the phone. His assessment, as we have seen, was that Dad most likely had a vascular dementia, probably caused by mini-strokes, and that Mum was probably in the early stages of Alzheimer's.

But again this remark about Mum was just a side observation. No healthcare professional ever showed more than this kind of incidental interest in Mum's mental health. I feel angry about that. As her dementia became more marked, I reported it to her GP but this did not result in any referral to a mental health professional. Perhaps this was another reason why we didn't see their sudden deterioration coming. At least three professionals, while visiting Dad, had observed Mum and noticed signs of dementia. None of them had taken any action. None at all. Mum's problems can't be too serious then, we reasoned, or surely they would be doing something. Wouldn't they?

The downside of getting the mental health professionals involved was that though Dad received a diagnosis, we were then told that nothing could be done. No treatment, no follow up, nothing. The diagnosis itself had been a shock to me, taking Dad out of the domain of 'getting old and depressed' to a more sinister and threatening place. But to find we would be travelling to that dark place with no medical help – what was the use of all these professionals?

Help at home

The upside of Jane's involvement was to initiate some help for Mum and Dad at home. Someone in 'the system' finally recognised the signs that they were struggling. Jane referred Mum and Dad to that wonderful organisation, Crossroads, set up originally to support carers. Crossroads, it turned out, could provide practical help (though not cleaning) but also saw itself as a befriending organisation and would take clients shopping or for a walk, for instance, or sit and have a chat and a cup of tea. Unlike 'the system' which tends to see people as bodies to be cleaned and fed, they put the emphasis on the client as a person with emotional as well as physical needs.

I had a long phone chat with one of the Crossroads managers who was familiar with people like Mum who need but don't want help. Once again we were up against the same questions that had floored Dad: what specifically would help them cope? Would Mum like to go shopping? the manager asked. Maybe, I thought. She certainly used to enjoy those visits to the Grafton Centre but the last time she'd been out of the house had been to buy me a birthday card for my 60th birthday and that was nearly three months before. What about preparing meals? the manager pursued. Mmm.

It had been a long time since either Mum or Dad had done any real cooking. We moved on to laundry. Now that was an area I hadn't really paid much attention to. And changing their bed linen. I realised I had no idea how they'd been managing – maybe they hadn't been changing it at all. Yes, I said, that was definitely something Crossroads could help with.

Enter Charmain

The manager duly visited Mum and Dad, filled out a form, put together a 'care plan', (Dad was down as Mum's carer by this time), and the first visit from Charmain, our assigned carer, was fixed. Mum, I now realise, was hazy as to what was going on. As the appointed day for Charmain's visit approached I realised I didn't know where Mum and Dad kept their clean sheets.

Asking Mum resulted in hostility and accusations of interfering, another sign, if I'd read it properly, that she was confused – she probably didn't know herself where the clean sheets were – and was embarrassed at being asked. Their bed was their business and no-one else's. Even if the sheets were never changed. But as usual I sidestepped thinking about the source of this symptom. Instead I took practical action: with some trepidation I brought over sheets and a duvet cover from home and put them in a prominent place for Charmain to find. And stuck some instructions on the washing machine about which programme to use.

On the day of Charmain's first visit, after she'd been there a while, I went round to see how things were going. Charmain had changed the bed, putting on the sheets and duvet cover I'd brought over. And Mum was enchanted. She proudly took me up to view the new bed, clearly having no idea I was admiring my own bed linen. Yet another sign I ignored. So charmed was I by Mum's pleasure at the sight of my clean sheets on her bed, that I didn't follow through and ask what could be going on in her head, such that she didn't realise what had happened.

For her part, Charmain was simply brilliant. Over the weeks and months, right up to the time they went into the home, she did the laundry, changed the sheets, helped unpack the online shop, helped Mum tidy up. But most impressive: she laughed and joked with Mum and Dad, made them cups of tea, chatted with them about her life, respected their different personalities, brightened up their life. This was exactly the kind of help they needed and for that I was hugely grateful.

2007: the signs become more obvious

In spite of all our best efforts, slowly but surely the edifice was crumbling. By 2007 the signs loomed larger as Mum forgot, for example, that perishable goods had to be put into the fridge. I got used to putting milk away but one day I opened a kitchen drawer, sniffed, rummaged around and found a piece of raw fish, part of a packet of frozen cod portions that had been opened then put back in the drawer instead of the freezer. More disturbing was that Mum didn't see the problem – she who in her right mind used to write dates on every fresh and frozen food item that came into the house. Suddenly I was having to explain the absolute basics of housekeeping, and she responded as if I was telling her something strange and new.

I noted all this, was surprised by it, took practical steps to sort it out, but didn't dwell on what must be happening to Mum's mind for her to respond so out of character. Even at this late stage it was still so much less painful to treat the symptoms than enquire too closely into what they meant.

Gallons of Gaviscon

Then there was the question of Mum's prescriptions. Once she'd stopped going out I'd taken to collecting her repeat prescriptions from the GP surgery and getting the medicines: thyroid medication and a large bottle of Gaviscon she needed to help her deal with a hiatus hernia. Or so I thought. I carefully made sure I got the right flavour of Gaviscon, and when I gave her the Boots bag containing her medication she always acted pleased and relieved, as though this was a major problem off her mind. I realise now, with hindsight, she still believed she normally collected her prescriptions herself. Each time I produced the bag, therefore, she was pleased because, as she saw it, I'd been kind enough to collect her prescription for her just this once.

One day for some reason I looked in a cupboard and there, on a shelf I didn't normally notice, I saw lined up not one, not two but nine bottles of Gaviscon. I'd been completely fooled by all that show of welcoming her prescription package every time. Here was clear evidence that she wasn't taking the medicine. Did she no longer need it? Had she forgotten she ever needed it? Had her symptoms disappeared?

A more worrying thought struck me – was she taking her thyroid medication, surely more important? I looked in the kitchen cupboard where I thought she kept her pills and couldn't find them. Where are your thyroid pills, Mum? She looked around vaguely but didn't seem to know. Have you been taking them? I've been taking them for years, was her reply. But where are they? She didn't know but kept saying of course she was taking them. She'd been taking them for years, therefore she must be taking them.

When she couldn't produce them she got upset. I guess I was forcing her confusion out into the open and that was very unsettling. I didn't persist but found the pills a few days later. And so began a regime of dosset boxes, a big one for Dad as he took a lot of medication, and a smaller version for Mum. And it became Dad's job to give Mum her thyroid medication in the morning when he took his own morning pills.

Dad didn't want the responsibility – of course he didn't, he was only too aware of his own mental struggles, but of the two of them, he was the one who still understood the concept of 'taking regular medication'. For Mum this knowledge appeared to have peeled off and floated away. And yet, in spite of these blanks in her brain, Mum continued to act much as her old self, assuming she was in control, believing she was doing all the household jobs she used to do. But I noticed that sometimes, no often, she didn't seem to know the time of day. I'd arrive in the early evening and she'd ask me if I'd had my breakfast. Of course I thought this was odd but chose to treat her question as a bit of a joke, not dwelling on what must be going on in her head.

It was the same when she'd say that people on TV, especially when their faces were in close up, were speaking directly to her. This definitely struck me as crazy, but again I didn't pursue these disturbing thoughts any further. Actually I wonder now if she was sometimes frightened by those faces on the screen looking directly at her. Dad said one day she had ripped the aerial out of the back of the TV: perhaps she was trying to chase them away.

Looking back to that time, I was operating on two distinct levels. An apparently matter-of-fact level on which I accepted Mum's oddities and did my best to deal with the practical consequences. And a deeper level of anguish and anxiety that I sensed but didn't allow to the surface very often. The image that comes to mind when I think back is of being trapped in a brightly lit cellar.

The 'crossie'

Something that crystallised the gradual yet irresistible march of Mum and Dad's mental breakdown was the Mail on Sunday general knowledge crossword. Known as 'the crossie', for years Mum and Dad worked on it, and other crosswords, together. Their house was a veritable library of reference books; they had to keep replacing their encyclopaedias and dictionaries, they'd get so tattered with use. Mum, in particular, loved 'looking things up';

she always went to bed late anyway, and at crossie time might stay up till the early hours hunting for the answer to a clue. When Dad got a computer – that was in his early 80s before low spirits set in – he'd look answers up on the internet. Mum never would though. I'd been surprised she'd shown no interest at all in learning about the computer preferring to hunt through books.

In those early days, when old age was being kept at bay, Dad would ring me on a Monday lunchtime and part of our chat involved getting me to help out with any remaining unanswered clues. As Dad got lower in spirits, though he stopped phoning, I was usually visiting them on a Wednesday evening – there were often a few clues left to help with. For Mum, being able to finish the crossie and post it off by the Thursday deadline was a weekly milestone, an achievement.

As Dad's spirits sank lower, he largely lost interest in the crossie but Mum nagged him into keeping it going. She needed him to do a few clues in order to get started. With some answers in she could continue on her own. Eventually, on a Sunday evening, I became the one who got the crossie started. Dad almost completely withdrew, saying he couldn't do it any more, though he could and did produce an answer now and then. Here was their key difference – whereas he would stop doing something because it was getting harder, say he couldn't when in fact he still could though with more difficulty, Mum wouldn't give up.

Until, that is, Nature decreed otherwise. In spite of her strong will Mum got to a stage where it might take her days to get one or two clues. I'd start the crossie off, do as many as I could and hand it over. She'd persevere till even she got discouraged. She simply couldn't do it any more. The newspapers piled up on a chair. The reference books lay silent and unopened. He'd withdrawn early from the fray; she'd fought on but had finally been beaten.

How do you make a cup of tea?

It was as the crossie dimmed and slowly disappeared that I could no longer ignore the way Mum had forgotten how to do simple everyday tasks such as making a cup of tea. What would you like? she'd say. I'll have a cup of tea, I'd reply, and she would busy about rather vaguely, then produce a jug and ask if that was right. Don't worry, I'll make it, I'd say, taking over. We shared a window cleaner, and he told me months later that one day he'd asked Mum for a glass of water and she'd produced a saucepan.

Though household objects and tasks were becoming hazy she would nag Dad, complaining he wasn't getting on with the vacuuming as he used to. In her mind, I realised later, she was probably living in a earlier time zone in which Dad was much younger and stronger. Life felt hard for her and she wanted his support whereas all he did was disappear to lie down. I hadn't learnt at this stage that it's better to go along with the world of a person with dementia rather than telling them they're mistaken. And so I'd try to tell her Dad was getting a bit too old to be pushing a heavy vacuum cleaner around. Clearly I needed to get them some help with the housework. As it was I was doing more and more of it myself as Mum continued to insist they were doing fine.

As 2007 went on, when Mum got dressed she'd sometimes put on several sets of clothes. None of this fazed Charmain, however; her training told her that what a mentally-confused person did was OK provided they weren't harming themselves. Jane, the CPN, had taken this view too. I eventually concluded that this robust attitude was part of the conventional wisdom that people are always better off being supported in their own homes, however oddly their dementia causes them to behave.

Charmain and I also had a number of discussions about Mum's pants and where she put them since there were rarely any in the laundry basket. I'd realised from reading a Guardian article written by a woman caring for her mother-in-law that Alzheimer's sufferers can forget routines such as wiping bottoms after going to the loo. Mum, I guess, saw her pants were dirty though she wasn't sure why. She was probably ashamed and that's why she hid her pants. Charmain and I would find them sometimes at the back of kitchen cupboards or stuffed behind a wardrobe. We found more later when Alan and I were clearing out their house.

Why we didn't see it coming

As 2007 ripened into summer and we approached those fateful weeks in July that brought life as Mum and Dad knew it to an end, their welfare was totally dominating my life. From noting the signs and putting them on the back burner, treating symptoms and not exploring the source, I was now confronted with signs of mental confusion at every turn.

For a while Mum had been sleeping in one of the small bedrooms at the back of the house. Dad had confessed that he didn't actually know when or where she slept, saying she was often roaming the house in the early hours. I could also see from the dosset boxes that Dad wasn't always giving Mum her pills. He couldn't, he said, because there was no morning routine any longer. Their ability to live independently was slowly falling apart.

More disturbing were those days, admittedly not many, when Mum would show signs of paranoia, telling Dad she didn't trust him. One evening when Dad and I had all their financial papers out – Dad had asked me to go through their savings accounts and organise the paperwork – she got upset at not being involved and said to me too: 'I don't trust you'. Maybe we were wrong not to include her, but by this stage I had Power of Attorney for her (though not yet for Dad) precisely because she had lost all understanding of financial affairs. Again, probably living in an earlier time zone, she seemed to feel that Dad ought to be managing their affairs, which were private, nothing to do with anyone else, including me.

In these small but multiplying ways I was witnessing the gradual breakdown of my mother's mind along with the dulling of my father's. And yet I still didn't put it that way to myself. In her own home, in that familiar environment that she had not left for nearly a year, Mum could still be plausible, still find her way around, still laugh and joke. And of course I was there to pick up the pieces. Against the odds, we were still clinging to the belief that they were muddling through after a fashion. We all had our heads down, concentrating like mad on just holding on. That's why we didn't see it coming.

Until that day when something happened, when Mum's knees were so painful she couldn't walk. Until Friday 13th 2007 when the not-very-helpful doctor visited. Until Sunday 15th July when she had two falls and was admitted to hospital 'for a few days'. Until that day she walked unsteadily out of the door of 24 Acrefield Drive, and never looked back. Never came back. The day their 'real' dementia began.

I told a friend I was writing this chapter, standing back from Mum and Dad's story and asking the question: why didn't we see it coming? To him it was obvious: 'Why would you want to see it coming?' Why indeed?

Chapter 12

Learning from dementia: losses and (a few) gains

As well as raising many questions, dementia also teaches many lessons. When this story started, around 2005, I knew next to nothing about dementia in any of its forms. Nor, so far as I'm aware, did either of my parents even though they may already have been affected in ways that were not yet obvious. Living with dementia has been a big learning experience for all of us.

For sufferers from Alzheimer's, or a similar type of dementia, like Mum, much of the learning, I guess, lies in adapting to having no medium or short term memory and the confusion that must entail. It's very hard for us outsiders to imagine what it's like not to remember what's just happened, not once, not occasionally, but all the time. Maybe you realise eventually that there's no point in trying to remember and that life is more comfortable if you give up the struggle to do what your brain will no longer allow. After all, this is how we cope if we become physically disabled. If we can't walk we have to adapt to moving about in some other way: other people accept this as inevitable. Similarly for dementia: we on the outside need to respect sufferers' surrender to what is. That's part of our learning – that we need to adapt to our loved ones as they are not as they were.

For sufferers from Dad's kind of vascular dementia, the learning, I guess, may be more painful precisely because, in the earlier stages at least, there is often more awareness. In Dad's case there certainly was. He and fellow sufferers have to adapt to progressive impairment of higher functions of the brain: they find it much harder to plan, learn new things, concentrate, find words. But because the damage to their brain is initially more selective than in Alzheimer's, some may feel their mental deterioration more keenly. No wonder vascular dementia often goes hand in hand with depression.

Ten life lessons from living with dementia

My parents have not been able to report on how dementia has felt for them and what they learnt from living with failing brains. I can only say what I have learnt as a layperson without any special expertise aside from what I have participated in and observed:

1: There are different kinds of dementia with different effects

This was one of the first things I learnt: it seemed obvious to me that dementia was affecting Mum's and Dad's brains differently and at different speeds. So much so that early on I would explain Mum's behaviour to Dad by saying 'It's because she's got dementia', largely ignoring the fact that he had too, so much less dramatic did the early impact of his vascular dementia seem.

Dementia, we need to understand, is no more than a blanket term used to cover a whole range of mental deterioration, often in old age but not always. Some people are affected as early as their 60s or 50s, or occasionally earlier. There are many types of dementia and even the same type can affect different personalities at varying speeds and in distinct ways.

Alzheimer's disease is the dementia best known to the public: it's the commonest, accounting for two thirds of dementias in the over 65s in the UK, and the most fully covered in the media, particularly when it strikes well-known figures such as Iris Murdoch, Ronald Reagan and, more recently, Terry Pratchett and Margaret Thatcher. As we live longer and predictions of an 'Alzheimer's epidemic' proliferate, 'Alzheimer's' is becoming one of those scary terms, more so even than 'cancer', manipulated in media headlines to cause maximum dread.

Being such an avid magazine-reader Mum would have certainly seen some of these headlines and doubtless read articles about Alzheimer's. Enough for her to attribute to Alzheimer's what she saw as Dad's changes in personality in those last years. It is likely that they each perceived subtle changes in the other much earlier than we realised.

Mum was wrong, of course, and Dad didn't have Alzheimer's while she herself probably does, or if not Alzheimer's then a dementia with similar effects. There are a lot of 'probablys' in the dementia field. We may never know precisely what she is suffering from as a definitive diagnosis can only be made by examining her brain tissue after she dies. And what use will that be to her then? Or so I'm tempted to say though I guess examining her brain could help with dementia research.

Alzheimer's Research UK (formerly the Alzheimer's Research Trust) is one of the organisations trying to reduce the 'probablys' by discovering more about the causes of Alzheimer's with a view to developing possible treatments. The symptoms, they explain, are caused by 'nerve cells dying in regions of the brain and connections between nerve cells degenerating'. This process normally starts by damaging connections between nerve cells in the part of the brain affecting memory, gradually spreading to other areas and attacking different functions. In the present state of scientific knowledge we still don't know for certain what causes the nerve cells to die. 'Different types of protein deposits (amyloid plaques and tau tangles) accumulate in the brain of Alzheimer's patients, but it is not yet known whether these actually cause the disease or happen due to some other cause', the research experts say. Clearly there is much still to discover and the welcome news is that government research funding for dementia is doubling.

Dad's vascular dementia was caused in a different way, by problems in the supply of blood to his brain, but there are a number of ways this can happen, and consequently a number of types of vascular dementia, some common, some rare. Dr Dening suggested Dad's was caused by mini-strokes, though, so far as I know, this was a best guess, another 'probably'. As with Alzheimer's, nothing is certain. Dad's probable type of vascular dementia, known as multi-infarct dementia, affects the cortex, the folded outer layer of the brain associated with learning and attention, memory and language. As areas of the cortex are starved of blood the cells eventually die, though unless caused by a serious stroke the process will usually be gradual. Dad certainly didn't have a major stroke, nor did we see any minor ones, though they 'probably' happened. In the earlier stages, his decline seemed gradual to us on the outside, though even gradual may have been much more frightening than I'd realised to Dad who felt his diminishing powers at first hand.

Though I can't know for certain, I imagine that dementia for Mum and dementia for Dad have been very different experiences on the inside. True, vascular dementia sufferers sometimes also develop Alzheimer's; and many Alzheimer's sufferers are found at autopsy to have significant vascular disease too. But the way Mum and Dad's different dementias have shown up in their behaviour has certainly been different with Dad largely low-spirited and silent and keeping to his room and Mum lively and restless and very much an active player in her gradually shrinking world.

2: Only sufferers know how dementia feels

This second lesson is the most important yet the hardest for us outsiders to keep in mind: only sufferers know how dementia feels. Because we can't get into each other's heads, even doctors and researchers who specialise in Alzheimer's or other dementias can't know how it feels to be a sufferer. The people who know, like my Mum and Dad, can't really tell us, though some do try, often younger sufferers, diagnosed with early onset (defined as under 65 years old) forms of the disease. A big learning is therefore to be aware of our ignorance. Our brain is the organ that controls all the major functions of our body. What we know about how it feels to sufferers when this control centre starts to break down is tiny compared to what we don't.

I've learnt therefore to keep an open mind and not make easy assumptions about how sufferers must feel and what they can and can't do. This is not easy, so used are we to judging others based on how we see things. One person who keeps reminding me that I don't, and can't, know how dementia feels is Richard Taylor, an American organisational psychologist first diagnosed with 'dementia, probably of the Alzheimer's type' at age 58. Richard has written extensively about his experiences of the earlier stages of this life-shattering condition. 'We are seldom seen post-diagnosis', he says poignantly of the way a diagnosis of Alzheimer's too often means sufferers are written off as if they are already as good as dead and the rest of their life has no value.

Richard Taylor asks many challenging questions: 'Could we possibly grow as a human being post-diagnosis?' he wonders, a question that gets to the heart of our fear of dementia. Here is a man who has received a sentence of hard labour with the prospect of a complete brain shut down to look forward to, proposing there can be a life with Alzheimer's. He is also aware that we on the outside find it more comfortable to shut out such ideas and concentrate on practicalities: 'At best, the professionals on my team provide lists to my caregivers on how to keep me from hurting myself and others…', he mourns. What he craves is to be able to 'find the books on how I can live with my disease. How can I be enabled, not disabled, by my caregivers to truly be all that I can be at any given moment of my life, even with this disease?'

You can learn a lot from Richard Taylor's writings, not least that we need to listen more to those who know at first hand.

3: People with dementia are still individuals and can retain strong personalities

This lesson is an extension of the last. My Mum and Dad had very different personalities when they were mentally fit. And they continued to have very different personalities when they became mentally disabled.

Dad was mild and easy-going but tended to go for a quiet life, taking the line of least resistance. In his later years, he was also conscientious, paid attention to detail and enjoyed keeping life in order. Once his dementia began seriously to bite there was no quiet life, no easy way out, nor was he capable of keeping life in order as he'd done in the past. His response was depression and withdrawal from the fray. That's my view, a view from the outside, anyway.

Mum was tougher (and still is: 'I'm a toughie' she said out of the blue the other day), with strong opinions, opinionated sometimes, curious about people, private, preferring to cope with ill health herself rather than consulting doctors, prickly if she caught the faintest whiff of criticism. Her response to her different dementia has been to live with it as if it's normal, remaining curious, prickly and tough even as she loses her grip on the moment by moment details of life. Again that's my second hand view, a view from the outside.

But what is sure is that dementia did not reduce them to being 'the same' any more than it made them 'the same' as any of their fellow residents in the Dementia Unit. They and the people they have been living with all suffer from some disorder of the brain, that's one thing they definitely have in common. But just as dementias differ significantly so do sufferers. No one person's brain is identical to anyone else's. Therefore no one dementia sufferer can have the same dementia experience as another.

Think about it: we all have different life experiences that are somehow 'stored' in our brains. Each dementia sufferer, therefore, starts the process with a differently furnished brain, different abilities, different memories, different fears and feelings. Thus, though the physical side, the process of damage to the nerve cells and their connections, will be similar across individuals, the resulting behaviour is likely to differ depending on the individual brain, the rate and pattern of nerve cell degeneration together with what 'content' was there to start with. In this way dementia, the breaking up of the mind, is different to, say, breaking a leg. Where human legs are, to all intents and purposes, pretty similar across individuals, human brains, with their different 'content', will show much more variation as they deteriorate.

This means we need to maintain a clearer distinction than doctors and researchers often do between the general and the individual. Though we can generalise about people with dementia and say they get confused and their memory is badly impaired because of a particular type of deterioration of the brain, the way this manifests in any one individual will be particular to that person.

This I've learnt at first hand through frequent visits to my parents and their fellow residents over several years. Individual variation is particularly marked in the area of speech. Some residents go along Dad's route and rarely speak at all. But even people who don't speak, don't speak in their own individual ways. Or rather their reticence seems different from the outside. One man softens his silence with smiles, for instance, while others can seem more irascible, as though they are holding back and will only speak if strongly provoked. Of course from the inside that's probably not what's happening: maybe the irascible-seeming ones are frustrated at not being able to find their words.

Certainly Dad sometimes seemed on the brink of speaking. I would wait expectantly but nothing came. Yet, when the urge was strong enough, he could speak. When Mum had one of her falls, for instance, he was next to her and witnessed it close up, seeing the blood all over her face. She was taken to hospital, and that evening, Dad asked one of the carers about her and whether she was still in hospital. He found the power of speech when he really needed it.

Once you can't take speech for granted, you become more aware of the expressive power of silence. One beautifully dressed resident who had completely lost all power of speech and most movement sat silently in her wheelchair, a vision of elegance and grace.

With others who appear to have lost their power of speech and seem incapable of conversation, I've noticed that if carers choose a time when all is quiet to chat to them, sometimes they show they do understand and can respond, that they are capable against appearances of a two-way conversation, however limited.

Some like Mum are losing the power of speech slowly but that does not mean they don't try to communicate. Mum engages in conversation even if no-one can understand what she is talking about beyond the first word or two of any sentence. I don't know if she's aware she often isn't making herself understood. For me it doesn't really matter any more – just being together and exchanging snatches of simple chat is communication enough.

Others are not silent at all. They speak fluently though sometimes what they say can sound confused or repetitive or suggest they're mentally in a different time zone. Among those who do speak easily the stronger personalities can be loud or disruptive; on occasions they provoke reactions in others. The quieter ones can mutter in annoyance; there are little spats sometimes. Just like in ordinary life.

4: Dementia is probably more frightening for sufferers than we imagine

My original formulation of this learning was that 'Dementia doesn't have to be frightening', by which I meant, I now realise, that dementia isn't so frightening to me, having seen it at such close quarters. However mentally disabled, my Mum and Dad remained recognisably themselves. For me, the slow deterioration of their brains has been sad. But not scary.

Which is all well and good, but, as Richard Taylor points out, so many conversations around Alzheimer's and dementia more generally centre round the observations and concerns of us, the outsiders, relatives, caregivers, doctors, researchers. Everyone but the sufferers themselves, those who experience the condition at first hand.

He's right, of course. Dementia may not be so frightening for me as an onlooker; but how frightening is it for sufferers? I thought back to some of the earlier days and how upset Dad would get if he felt he wasn't believed when he claimed something had happened. There was that time described in Chapter 6 when he talked about there having been 24 hours of strikes in the home. My reaction was to try to figure out what had happened that he might have interpreted as strikes. But to him my well-meaning efforts just showed I didn't believe him. I remember him trying to get Mum to confirm there had indeed been strikes. He insisted, I see now but didn't then, because if he was wrong, if there had been no strikes, then his mind was playing tricks on him – and that must have been frightening.

So yes, dementia is probably more frightening for sufferers than we imagine. That is my revised formulation, reinforced by Oliver James's book 'Contented Dementia', based on the work of his mother-in-law, Penny Garner, who has developed a method (Specialised Early Care for Alzheimer's or SPECAL) that caregivers can adopt to help some Alzheimer's sufferers at least to live with their dementia with less fear.

We can't know what it feels like to live with a failing mind unless it happens to us, but we can be helped to understand something of the effects of dementia. Penny Garner uses analogy to explain her approach: if we think of our memory as like a photograph album, then the album is the place where memories are stored, and the photographs are individual memories. The early pages house long ago memories, and the later pages the most recent.

A photo, or stored memory, she suggests, has two elements: the facts, what the photo represents, the place or person or situation we remember, and the emotions associated with these facts. Thus we have positive, happy memories (or photos), difficult, sad photos, and many in between.

'When dementia begins', Oliver James reports, 'a single, striking change happens in what gets stored: the factual content is not registered, only the feelings…When this starts happening, Penny describes the dementia-induced feelings-only fact-free photographs as 'blanks'.'

At first these 'blanks', these occasions when you can recall feelings but don't have any facts to make sense of them, are few. But eventually sufferers have pages of their album, or memory, full of blanks. They know things have been happening; they still have feelings but they don't know what about. 'In due course the person will find themselves unable to ignore or conceal from others that they are missing information that they need to make sense of what they are currently doing.' And this, I imagine, is very scary. Penny Garner suggests that, faced with this realisation, sufferers can feel enormous distress and panic, a state she labels as a 'red blank', 'a wholly unacceptable feeling of ill-being, normally restricted to highly traumatic, relatively rare events.'

As Oliver James explains it: 'To be confronted by a series of red blanks is a nightmare that no person without dementia can fully appreciate – a series of photographs containing wholly unacceptable feelings and entirely devoid of facts to explain where such feelings have come from.' Understandably sufferers are agitated and upset: what they may then do is search for some explanation for their feelings so they can try and put things right and get back on an even keel. And how do they search? By leafing through the earlier pages of their album, where many of the photographs are still intact. There they may find some upsetting memory from the past which they assume is happening in the present (the ability to exist in different time zones at the same time, the present and a long distant past, was one of the characteristics of dementia I observed very early on when Mum was first in hospital). But they soon come up against the reactions of non-demented family members or caregivers who have no idea what they are talking about or trying to do, and judge them as very confused.

If what they are trying to do seems particularly crazy, or dangerous, or makes them appear very upset and agitated, some sufferers are given strong anti-psychotic drugs. Such drugs are normally given for schizophrenia, even though dementia and schizophrenia are very different disorders of the brain. They can often make a bad situation worse. We now know that anti-psychotics have precipitated death in a significant number of dementia sufferers. Clearly dementia can be very scary. I'm grateful that neither of my parents has been agitated enough for doctors to consider prescribing such medication.

Penny Garner's method of helping people live well with dementia is based on her attempts over many years to understand sufferers' response to 'red blanks'. Her approach, which requires both preparation and patience, lets the sufferer, whom she calls the 'client', take the lead. Caregivers don't contradict or try to drag them back into the 'real world' but rather they enter their world as far as possible aiming to reassure and restore the client's confidence so that their blanks are not an upsetting red but a benign green. 'Green blanks' are comfortable, acceptable blanks: 'Feeling good and not knowing why is quite a different proposition to feeling bad and not knowing why', James says.

The alternative that many sufferers adopt is to withdraw by 'closing their album' altogether rather than face the horror of feeling and not knowing, descending into the near vegetative state in which some elderly dementia sufferers end their days. And for those who remain agitated, their 'challenging behaviour' is liable to have them labelled 'hard to manage', a problem to which no-one currently has a solution.

Penny Garner has worked successfully with Alzheimer's sufferers over a long time, as well as passing on her SPECAL approach to many carers. Her suggestions and insights are hugely valuable, particularly in caring for people in the earlier stages of the disease. But she is still an outsider, though a knowledgeable and sympathetic one.

Richard Taylor gives some idea of how 'blanks' feel on the inside, though he does not use that terminology. His analogy is different: he talks about the 'corridors of his mind', where he walks when he is alone, opening doors and finding to his relief that long-stored memories are still there. As he moves towards the present, however, he finds more and more 'empty rooms' (something like Penny Garner's 'blanks'), which are dark: 'they offer no clue, other than the label on the door, what they once contained…It is very un-nerving to be in the midst of a conversation and all of a sudden need to open the door to a room to access its contents and – the room is dark. I don't have a clue.' Dementia is unnerving, frightening.

Though he doesn't talk about 'red blanks' or feelings without facts, a similar agitation is evident: 'I pause in my conversation and search for clues and connections. I race up and down the corridors of my mind, frantically seeking to make sense of what's going on around me. Sometimes this process makes me even more lost, and I become lost about why I am lost!'

Eventually he finds himself totally confused, 'forced to pause and try to recall why I am here. But the blank doors around me give me no clues.'

'Red blanks', 'empty rooms', 'blank doors', different images to help us try and understand what dementia does to the brain and how that feels. Darkness and emptiness are recurring themes. Another sufferer whose writings provide us with clues as to how dementia feels from the inside is Robert Davis: 'Wandering around and restlessness is one of the by-products of Alzheimer's disease. Many people have tried to guess why Alzheimer's disease patients are so restless and want to walk around at all hours of the day and night. I believe I may have a clue. When the darkness and emptiness fill my mind, it is totally terrifying. I cannot think my way out of it. It stays there, and sometimes images stay stuck in my mind. The only way that I can break this cycle is to move.'

Clearly dementia can be very scary, more so than we imagine, making enlightened help and support hugely important to sufferers' well-being.

5: We need to find new ways of communicating with dementia sufferers

This next lesson, that conversing with people with dementia requires us to be imaginative and find new ways of communicating, took me a while to grasp. In the early days I continued to communicate with Mum and Dad more or less as usual. And because Dad was the one who seemed to still know where he was and what was going on, he was the one I plagued with questions. My motives were well-intentioned: I wanted him to give his opinion on matters that concerned him and Mum. Should we sell or rent their house? Was he OK? What else did he need to be as comfortable as possible in the home? Did he still remember the house in Acrefield Drive? That was important to me – though I knew Mum had forgotten the house I needed to believe that Dad still remembered their home and all the time we'd spent there together as a family.

Quickly frustrated by being asked questions Dad made it as clear as he could that this was not the way to communicate when dealing with someone with a wobbly mind. And when I didn't get the message he adopted a strategy of bowing his head to signal that he was withdrawing from the interrogation.

By the time I came to read about Penny Garner's SPECAL method in 'Contented Dementia' I'd finally grasped the first of her three commandments for working with people who can't store new information:

Don't ask questions

(the other two are: 'Learn from the expert – your client' and 'Never contradict'.)

I had finally understood why we shouldn't ask questions though the reason should have been obvious much sooner: we should avoid questions, particularly about the present and recent past, because much of the time dementia sufferers like Mum and Dad don't know the answers.

One reason it took me so long to grasp this lesson is that questions come naturally to me. I'm interested in other people and curious. I want to know things. It was a big learning, therefore, to let go of my old ways and find a new approach to relating. I gradually got better at letting Mum and Dad and their fellow residents take the lead, trying to latch on to what they were saying. Making statements that might draw them in to what I'm saying rather than questions that remind them of what they don't know. If they're clearly in another time zone, accepting it without comment. Being matter-of-fact and reassuring. This is a world of conversations with a light touch – talking for the joy of sharing a moment together rather than for the literal meaning of the words.

6: As dementia worsens, staying in your own home may not be the best option

As highlighted by my own internal struggles when starting to look for a care home for Mum, there is an accepted wisdom, not just in the caring field but in the world more generally, that people are always best looked after in their own homes. An assumption that any other solution is second best; an assumption I'd shared without thinking. In many cases this assumption is right, particularly as there are good and bad care homes, and many in between. Finding yourself trapped in a bad home is a nightmare we all want to avoid, for our loved ones, and for ourselves.

In caring for dementia sufferers the accepted wisdom needs to be re-examined, I learnt early on, not least because there comes a time, for Alzheimer's sufferers definitely and for other types of dementia in the later stages, where they lose awareness of where they are. When Mum went into hospital on the Sunday of that Crisis Weekend in 2007, I naturally assumed she'd come back home. But that was because I was looking at her with my mental capacities not hers. Where I had a mental framework in which to fit her hospital stay, to my great surprise, she had none. She didn't know she was in hospital, yet never asked where she was or when she'd be going home. All these concerns were gone already but until then, as her daughter and frequent visitor and carer, I'd had no idea.

Though I didn't think of it like this at the time, I subsequently asked myself: how is it we insist people who have lost awareness of where they are are necessarily better off in their own homes? They may be, of course, but we can't assume without question that where they lived when mentally fit is the best place for them when mentally frail.

According to Oliver James, his mother-in-law, Penny Garner, considers we assume their own home must be the best place because we are so caught up with our own feelings of guilt or distress or uncertainty that we don't see the situation from the sufferer's point of view. From her experience there comes a stage with Alzheimer's or similar dementias, where it is 'imperative for the client's well-being that they move into a nursing home'. Back in 2007 I had no idea that Mum had reached that stage, and yet she settled into the care home as though it was a release. I guess the preceding months had been a tough struggle with an everyday domestic world that was becoming less and less comprehensible. Since she's been in the home I've been absolutely convinced she's in the right place, and is better off than if she'd stayed in their own home with carers coming in. Where she is, she has space, stimulation from carers and what Penny Garner calls 'just the right level of companionship' from fellow residents: they give each other company but don't press each other to make sense. And because Dad got himself into the home too, and eventually his own dementia got worse, she regained his familiar presence, even though she regularly expressed surprise that he was there.

Penny Garner talks of a tipping point, the point at which 'the balance of benefits to the client of remaining at home is just beginning to tip in favour of moving'. Her advice to caregivers is to prepare and be on the look out for this point. Visit homes before a sudden crisis means you're rushed into a less than perfect decision. Choose the home in advance so that when the time comes you are confident you have chosen a good home and the choice feels right.

Heeding her advice does not automatically mean that all dementia sufferers should be in a home. But rather, that going into a home may, at some point, be a good option and one that should be seriously considered as actually being in the best interests of the sufferer. In our case, events occurred so quickly with Mum and Dad that we didn't have a chance to go through the whole process Penny Garner recommends. I have always felt that we were very lucky to find such a good home for Mum, and then Dad, at short notice and with minimum fuss. A light, bright, friendly home that I can visit without a heavy heart.

7: Life is precious – and precarious

This next lesson is a constant reminder that our identity is precarious depending as it does on the well functioning of our brain. All those past experiences that have made us who we are lie in our memory. If we have no memory, who are we? A disease that attacks our brain, our control centre, is a strong threat to our identity. Richard Taylor expresses this threat forcefully: 'I am starting to fear the coming of the end of me. Not the *death* of me, but the *end* of me as I know myself and as others have known me.'

Being around people whose identity is precarious, who don't know where they are, who are not clear who they are is a reminder of the fragility of life. Life is precious and precarious. I am reminded of this lesson every time I visit the care home. This reminder to seize my own life with both hands and live it to the full while I am strong and well has been a gift to me from Mum and Dad and their fellow residents. Though their minds are damaged they can still express warmth and concern. It can feel sometimes as though they are cheering me on from the sidelines to which they have necessarily withdrawn. I am grateful to them for all they give me.

8: Dementia is disturbing in an age of doers and achievers

Another reminder, this time that we live in an age that celebrates doers and achievers, an age in which being busy is a badge of honour. As a chronic, incurable disease that most often occurs in old people, dementia is disturbing, challenging as it does the ideas of everlasting youth and constant progress with which we protect and delude ourselves.

Dementia also challenges an illusion that many of us maintain, that we'll grow old gracefully and die a quiet, dignified death surrounded by our loved ones. The government colludes in this illusion: its discussion document on reviewing the care and support system focused on people remaining 'independent, active and healthy…throughout their lives.' Even while discussing the need for a new care and support system, it depicted the reality of ageing with rose-tinted spectacles.

Of course some people do live independent, active and healthy lives to the end. And we all hope to be among those hale and hearty seniors. But people with dementia don't. Dementia is a chronic illness with no cure: a long walk into increasing darkness in which the self is gradually but relentlessly lost. No wonder dementia is disturbing, tapping as it does into our basic fear of oblivion.

Our care system is brisk, and in some ways inhuman, focusing as it does on the physical side of care, largely ignoring psychological and emotional needs. But how is it for those on the receiving end? How do we think it feels for a dementia sufferer, living alone, to receive a string of short visits from carers who could well be different from week to week, or even from day to day? What use is it to be washed and dressed when you are frightened and need human contact and reassurance?

People caring for loved ones with dementia, or sufferers themselves, are speaking out much more these days – John Suchet, for example, about his wife, Terry Pratchett about himself – challenging our fears and appealing to our humanity. Dementia may be disturbing in an age that celebrates doers and achievers. But should we not be facing up to why?

9: With some exceptions, medics are not interested in dementia

This is not a crusading memoir but on this topic I feel anger as well as some fear. My decision to tell Mum and Dad's dementia story started with a doctor's visit which made me very angry. So much so I made notes, a long list of all that was wrong with that consultation with my Mum, from clueless communication to haughty dismissal of dementia into the domain of social care. Thus I learnt this lesson very early on: with some exceptions, medics are not interested in dementia. I say 'with some exceptions', because I know there are doctors out there who are much less dismissive of disorders of the brain in old people. It just so happens that I haven't met any of them.

What I've observed instead in the medical profession is a breathtaking level of ignorance, or is it unawareness, of what it means to suffer from dementia. Perhaps that shouldn't be surprising given lesson 2: 'Only sufferers know how dementia feels'. Mum was in A&E recently after a fall, and was generally well-treated. The staff 'knew' she suffered from dementia, insofar as they had been told. But this 'knowledge' didn't translate itself into their behaviour. They followed their communication training, which says, these days, you speak directly to the patient; this is the way to treat them with respect. 'Lift your arm for me, Mary'. Nothing happens. 'Your arm, lift your arm'. The fact that at a certain stage of dementia, simple instructions like this are not understood doesn't seem to occur to otherwise competent nurses and doctors. Aren't they supposed to know something about human brains?

Not that it's easy. On that same occasion, once Mum was patched up, though she'd arrived by ambulance the hospital weren't keen to provide transport back to the home. To them, a 92 year old with dementia and a swollen head, on a dark, rainy night, should be able to get back by car. My car was in the hospital car park. 'Let's give it a try', I said to the carer who'd accompanied Mum in the ambulance and was still there. Actually it was a nightmare, out there in the rain and the darkness with Mum crying out in pain, panic and confusion, no-one from the hospital offering any help at all. We couldn't get her into the car because she kept both her feet glued to the ground: 'Come on, Mum, lift your foot...' We fell into the same trap: asking her to do what she couldn't understand, then repeating it when she didn't comply. Finally we realised and found another way.

I have no criticism of Mum and Dad's physical care by the doctors who have been called periodically to check out this or that symptom. They are invariably polite and thorough, going through their diagnostic checklist of physical systems. What I simply can't fathom, it seems so bizarre, is the way they pay minute attention to every physical system in the body, yet do not even mention the fact that these are people with extensive dead areas in their brains. It's as though there is a tacit agreement that they will visit dementia sufferers provided no-one mentions the D-word!

Ros Coward, who wrote a Guardian column for some years, about her mother's growing dementia, calls it a 'colossal failure at the heart of the health service'. Like me she has found that 'time and again when my mother comes into contact with the health services they completely overlook her dementia'. In the home medication is given out by Senior Carers whereas her mother was still living in the community where health professionals kept 'issuing her with complicated instructions about how to take pills, expecting her to remember to come to clinics and appointments, asking her questions about her own condition – none of which she can do'.

Dementia sufferers can fare even worse in hospitals. A recent Alzheimer's Society survey showed that 90 per cent of nurses felt that working with people with dementia was challenging. Even though dementia is an illness as much as heart disease or cancer. More than half of the carers questioned said that staying in hospital had made their client's dementia symptoms worse. And there were horror stories too of patients whose dementia meant they couldn't feed themselves, not eating or drinking because staff didn't notice their needs.

As a layperson I have tried to come up with reasons why dementia is the 'elephant in the room' with doctors, who are intelligent people, in other respects probably doing an excellent job. Is it that dementia can't be cured and they feel a sense of failure? Possibly, though this is also true of many chronic conditions. They can't cure diabetes or asthma either. Do they not know how to communicate with a patient with dementia? Perhaps, though it's perfectly possible to learn. Is it some primal fear – as though the condition could be contagious? Or is it economic? By ignoring the fact that dementia is a mental health issue, and directing sufferers to social care, the health service neatly evades having to pay for their care. Does it suit doctors to collude with this pretence?

Though I have a lot of respect for Western medicine, the treatment of dementia is clearly an area where our test-based, drug-based dualistic approach is inappropriate. That the medics have nothing to offer dementia sufferers and effectively pretend dementia is not a mental health issue is certainly the scariest lesson I've learnt. We, whose minds are well-functioning, can see how badly the mental health needs of dementia sufferers are served by doctors. We are the ones with awareness of how awful it will be if we ever become sufferers ourselves.

10: There is wonderful kindness in the world

On the plus side I have come across wonderful warmth, dedication and kindness, particularly among carers. They have a difficult job and deserve more recognition through better pay. They are also a huge source of expertise in how dementia actually plays out in different individuals. Their expertise should be recognised and tapped.

What's beautiful to watch sometimes is the way the very best of them treat each resident as a valuable person; they don't give up on them and they show exemplary patience. When Mum first went to live in the home there was a resident who never left her room: her door was often open, and she would wail periodically. I assumed she was in great distress. After a while she died, and the next day I talked to a couple of the carers who said how much they'd miss her and what a great character she'd been. By spending so much time with her, they'd got past the wailing which, for all I know might have been involuntary. They hadn't given up on her and had been rewarded. It was a lesson in not making assumptions, and one I hope I'll never forget.

RESOURCES
Learn more about dementia

Some facts and figures

The Alzheimer's Research Trust (now Alzheimer's Research UK) commissioned the Health Economics Research Centre at Oxford University to produce a report on the economic cost of dementia to the UK. The results, published in the Research Trust's report 'Dementia 2010', show dementia to be one of the biggest medical challenges of the 21st century:

- Over 820,000 people in the UK live with Alzheimer's and other dementias.

- Dementia costs the UK economy £23 billion per year: more than cancer and heart disease combined.

- Dementia research is severely underfunded, receiving 12 times less support than cancer research.

The government has recently announced that funding for dementia research will increase from £26.6 million in 2010 to £66 million by 2015.

The Alzheimer's Society

Key organisation in the dementia field. Very helpful and active in giving information and support as well as sponsoring research. Local branches all over the country. Visit their website:

www.alzheimers.org.uk/

The Alzheimer's Society produces a series of downloadable factsheets on key questions and issues relating to dementia including factsheets on the most common forms of dementia:

- Alzheimer's

- Vascular dementia

- Dementia with Lewy bodies

- Frontotemporal dementia including Pick's disease

Talking Point is the Alzheimer's Society online forum where people with dementia and their carers can share experiences and seek advice. The Society's report 'Dementia 2012' assesses how well people are living with dementia in 2012 in England, Wales and Northern Ireland.

NHS Choices

For information on dementia from NHS Choices (the online official gateway to the NHS and, it is claimed, the country's biggest health website giving wide-ranging information to allow us to make choices about our health), go to:

www.nhs.uk/dementia/Pages/dementia.aspx

Dementia UK

A national charity committed to improving the quality of life for all people affected by dementia. Initiatives include training and funding of Admiral Nurses, specialist mental health nurses who work within the NHS funded by Dementia UK. Go to:

www.dementiauk.org

Dementia UK run a phone and email helpline staffed by experienced Admiral Nurses. Call 0845 257 9406 or email direct@dementiauk.org

The Dementia Centre

Information and resources for people living with dementia, their carers and health professionals. Go to:

www.dementiacentre.com

Support for Carers

Carers Direct

Find out about Carers Direct from NHS Choices (click on Carers Direct from Home page (www.nhs.uk). You can call the Carers Direct helpline on 0808 802 0202 if you need help with your caring role and want to talk to someone about what options are available.

Carers UK

The UK voice of carers. Find out more at:

www.carersuk.org

Crossroads Care

Leading provider of practical care, support and respite for carers and those they care for. In April 2012 Crossroads Care merged with the Princess Royal Trust for Carers to form a new charity called Carers Trust. Go to:

www.crossroads.org.uk/

Department of Health

National Dementia Strategy

The National Dementia Strategy, the first ever in the UK, aims to transform the quality of dementia care. Laid out in a document published in February 2009, it sets out initiatives designed to make the lives of people with dementia, their carers and families, better and more fulfilled.

The National Dementia Strategy has been backed by £150 million over the first two years. The idea has been to increase awareness of dementia, ensure early diagnosis and intervention and radically improve the quality of care that people with the condition receive. Proposals include the introduction of a dementia specialist into every general hospital and care home and for mental health teams to assess people with dementia.

Find out more on the Department of Health website:

www.dh.gov.uk

Care Quality Commission

The body responsible for the quality of social care and care homes in the UK. To find social care services such as help at home or care homes and check their quality, go to:

www.cqc.org.uk/

Dementia Research

Alzheimer's Research UK

Alzheimer's Research UK, formerly the Alzheimer's Research Trust, see their research programmes as the best in their field offering real hope of making breakthroughs in the fight against dementia. See:

www.alzheimersresearchuk.org

Bradford Dementia Group

Established in 1992, a multi-disciplinary and multi-professional group committed to making a difference to policy and practice in dementia care. Mission: to work with practitioners and professionals to improve the quality of life and care for people with dementia and their families.

www.brad.ac.uk/health/dementia/

Lasting Power of Attorney

Lasting Power of Attorney is administered by the Office of the Public Guardian, the administrative arm of the Court of Protection and an Executive Agency within the Ministry for Justice. See:

www.justice.gov.uk/about/opg

A Lasting Power of Attorney (LPA) is a legal document that enables a person who has capacity and is over 18 (Donor) to choose another person or people (Attorney(s)) to make decisions on their behalf. There are 2 different types of LPA:

- A property and financial affairs LPA is for decisions about finances, such as selling the Donor's house or managing their bank account; and

- A health and welfare LPA is for decisions about both health and personal welfare, such as where to live, day-to-day care or having medical treatment.

An Attorney is appointed to make decisions as if they were the Donor themselves and must act in the Donor's best interests.

An LPA **must** be registered with the Office of the Public Guardian (OPG) before it can be used. The Donor can register the LPA while they have capacity, or the Attorney can apply to register the LPA at any time. The <u>Registering a Lasting or Enduring Power of Attorney</u> page of the Office of the Public Guardian website has a pack available for download that contains the forms required to register an LPA.

Some books

'*Alzheimer's from the Inside Out*', Richard Taylor, Health Professions Press, 2007

'*Contented Dementia*', Oliver James, Vermilion, 2008

'*Keeper: Living with Nancy: A Journey into Alzheimer's*', Andrea Gillies, Short Books, 2009

'*Living and Dying with Dementia: Dialogues about Palliative Care*', Neil Small, Katherine Froggatt and Murna Downs, Oxford University Press, 2007

'*Telling Tales about Dementia: Experiences of Caring*', edited by Lucy Whitman, Jessica Kingsley Publishers, 2010

'*The Year of Magical Thinking*', Joan Didion, Fourth Estate, 2005

'*Remind me who I am again*', Linda Grant, Granta, 1998

'*My Bonnie: How Dementia Stole the Love of my Life*', John Suchet, HarperCollins, 2010

'*Before I Forget*', Fiona Phillips, Preface, 2010

'*Tell Mrs Mill her Husband is Still Dead*', compiled by David Clegg (a collection of histories from people with dementia), Available from www.trebusprojects.org

'*My Journey into Alzheimer's Disease*', Robert Taylor, Tyndale House, 1989

Lightning Source UK Ltd.
Milton Keynes UK
UKOW05f0342180215

246416UK00009B/164/P